Drugs Wise

A practical guide for concerned parents about the use of illegal drugs

Melanie McFadyean

Illustrations by Oscar Zarate

Published in association with the Kaleidoscope Project

ICON BOOKS

Published in 1997 by Icon Books Ltd.,
Grange Road, Duxford, Cambridge CB2 4QF
e-mail: icon@mistral.co.uk

Distributed in the UK, Europe, Canada, South Africa and Asia by
the Penguin Group:
Penguin Books Ltd, 27 Wrights Lane, London W8 5TZ

Published in Australia in 1997 by Allen & Unwin Pty. Ltd.,
PO Box 8500, 9 Atchison Street, St. Leonards, NSW 2065

Cover design by Bill Mayblin
Design and layout by Christos Kondeatis and Zoran Jevtic
Edited by Philippa Brewster and Jeremy Cox
Picture researcher: Vivien Adelman

ISBN 1 874166 83 8

Printed and bound in Great Britain by The Bath Press

Contents

4   **Acknowledgements**

7   **Chapter One**
From cradle to rave: starting to understand the drug culture

16   **Chapter Two**
Sniff: solvents and volatile substances

28   **Chapter Three**
Puff: cannabis

59   **Chapter Four**
Rave: the dance drugs – ecstasy, amphetamine and LSD

101   **Chapter Five**
Beyond the rave: heroin, cocaine and crack

143   **Chapter Six**
Smoke and drink: tobacco and alcohol

149   **Chapter Seven**
Drugs and the law

169   **Glossary**

189   **Where to go for help**

Acknowledgements

My special gratitude goes to the parents and young people who gave me their time for the interviews in this book. Special thanks also to Sally Murray of Kaleidoscope for her help and support and to Philippa Brewster and Jeremy Cox for their editing.

Thanks very much to the Institute for the Study of Drug Dependence (ISDD): to Harry Shapiro for approving the factual content of the book, to the librarians who tirelessly provided me with many dozens of research papers for the extensive background reading and to executive director Anna Bradley for her help. Thanks also to Steve Taylor and Anette Dale Pereira of SCODA. Thanks to Rosalie Chamberlain of Kaleidoscope, Professor Griffith Edwards of the National Addiction Centre at the Maudsley Hospital and Dr Penny Green of Southampton University for their insight and information. Thanks to Simon Flynn of Icon Books for compiling the glossary and doing additional research. Thanks to the librarians at the National Children's Bureau. Thanks to Kim Longinotto and Nadine Cartner for their insights.

Thanks also to drugs workers from all over the UK, particularly to Colin Wisely of Unit 51, Kirklees; Mark Gillman and Jez Buffin of Lifeline Manchester; Colin Cripps of Network Drugs Advice Project; Kieran O'Hagan and Penny Cotton of Release; Willie MacBride of Glasgow Enhance; Crawford Bell of Edinburgh's Harm Reduction Team; Phil Harris of the Bristol Drug Project; and Tim Bottomley of the Trafford Piper Project.

I have learned an enormous amount from the many research papers I have read by academics, criminologists, people from the fields of medicine and psychiatry and others from all over the world. These are too numerous to mention individually.

Books that were specially helpful or interesting included: *Young People and Heroin* by Geoffrey Pearson (Gower); *Living with Drugs* by Michael Gossop (Arena); *Street Drugs* by Andrew Tyler (Hodder and Stoughton); *Forbidden Drugs* by Philip Robson (Oxford University Press); *E for Ecstasy* by Nicholas Saunders (published by the author); *Drug Scenes*, a report by the Royal Institute of Psychiatrists (Gaskell); *Dope Girls* by Marek Kohn (Lawrence and Wishart); *Misuse of Drugs and Drug Trafficking Offences* by Rudi Fortson (Sweet and Maxwell); *Drugs and British Society* edited by Suzanne MacGregor (Routledge); *Taking Drugs Seriously* by Julian Cohen and James Kay (Thorsons); *Ceremonial Chemistry* by Thomas Szasz (Routledge and Kegan Paul); *Risk Takers: Alcohol, Drugs, Sex and Youth* by M. Plant (Routledge).

Among many reports which readers might like to look at are: *Common Illegal Drugs and Their Effects* (Parliamentary Office of Science and Technology, 1996); *Drug Use in England* (Health Education Authority, 1997); *Drug Usage and Drugs Prevention* (Home Office, HMSO); *Young People and Drug Taking: Facts and Trends* by John Balding (University of Exeter).

For further reading, ISDD have many excellent pamphlets and books aimed at the general public (see page $$ for address). Two major reports which readers may also like to look at are: NHS Health Advisory Service Thematic Review: *Children and Young People, Substance Misuse Services, The Substance of Young Needs* (Health Advisory Service); and *The Effectiveness of Services for Young Drug Users* (a study by MORI on behalf of the Department of Health's Task Force to Review Services for Drugs Misusers).

Melanie McFadyean

Foreword
by Adele Blakebrough

'I rarely managed to keep my cool at the sight of my handsome son lolling incoherently on his bed. I pleaded with him to stop, threatened to throw him out, promised him anything he wanted. I reasoned, wept, cold-shouldered, shouted – but nothing made any difference.'

Thus one of the dozens of parents who speak remorsefully, movingly and above all honestly, in the pages of this book. Nothing can dispel the dismay and the pain when a mother or father finds that a child is secretly using drugs. We all wish for the moon for our children. But there are many testimonies in these pages from those who discovered that, as they found out more about drugs, they also took the first and vital step in dealing with the problem: they could talk to their children.

This is a book primarily for parents. It does not offer a seven-step easy guide to stopping your child from taking drugs. That would be a fairy tale. But it does offer accurate information, true stories and the encouragement – based upon long experience and careful analysis – that very few ordinary, stable kids experience fatal or even seriously harmful effects from their drug taking.

It is because there are others for whom drug use indicates deep unhappiness and even suicidal tendencies that every parent needs to understand this subject in some depth. It may be too late when you actually discover that your child is one of the tens of thousands, more likely millions, who are experiencing illegal drugs in their teenage years. The time to prepare yourself is now; the need to insulate yourself against the wild and inaccurate reporting about drugs in the mass media is underlined every day.

I am delighted that the Kaleidoscope Project, which I run, has been given the opportunity to help with the production of this book. Based in Kingston-upon-Thames on the south-west edge of London, we have worked with all aspects of the drugs scene for 30 years: we have run education programmes in schools, trained drugs workers from numerous countries around the world, and taken heroin addicts through detoxification programmes. Every day, we offer care to 300 serious opiates users.

In those 30 years, we have debated every policy option and heard every emotional register. Today, as the government appoints its first Drugs Czar to co-ordinate policy on drugs, there is still an urgent need for clear, uncharged factual information that parents can rely on and that can actually help people to deal with a problem where in practice there are many ways forward. This is not a book which preaches a particular point of view about drugs, other than to say that accurate information and true facing up to what's going on are better guides for parents and for politicians than misinformation and hysteria.

Although aimed mainly at parents, I know that this book also passes another vital test: any teenager will find it authentic. It describes a world where young people consume an astonishing variety of illegal substances, mostly for fun or for entirely recognisable social reasons, never without some danger, but almost always without catastrophe. A child who takes drugs is not necessarily a deviant, a drop-out or sick; indeed, almost all of them are perfectly ordinary, healthy young people.

That is the central message in a book in which no punches are pulled, no make-believe indulged. Long experience tells me that this is the only way we can start to make a difference.

Rev Adele Blakebrough, Director, the Kaleidoscope Project, Kingston-upon-Thames. September 1997

Chapter One

From cradle to rave:

Starting to understand the drug culture

When I started work on this book I was no more of an expert on the subject of drugs than the next parent. But as a writer and journalist I am used to researching, and as a former teacher and *Just Seventeen* agony aunt I am used to teenagers and their fads, moods, enthusiasms, tantrums, sweetness and spots. So I had some of the necessary qualifications. I approached the subject with great interest, an open enough but averagely misinformed, typically bewildered and scared parent's mind. I think a lot of parents feel this way about the subject of their sons and daughters and drugs.

It doesn't help that we are bombarded with hyped-up media reports about young people and drugs. One headline sums it all up for me: 'Gymslip Junkies Sniff Dog Powder Love Potions'. If you unpack this ludicrous but alarming headline, what do you get? First of all we know that the drug taker is very young because she's in a 'gymslip'. Secondly she is way down the line with drugs – a 'junkie'. Thirdly she is sniffing, an activity guaranteed to inspire fear and dread. Fourthly her drug is a dog powder – weird, alarming bizarre – what will these young people not do the minute our backs are turned? Fifthly her drug is a 'love potion' – that means gymslip junkie is not only taking drugs but intending to have sex. And what is she sniffing? A potion, which adds a witchy, spooky dimension.

There she is: the all-in-one, all-purpose media creature, the appalling teenaged druggy. The effect on parents reading the headline is to feed the fears we quite rightly feel about our children taking drugs. But hold on. The real story, contrary to popular belief, is that there are in fact very few 'gymslip junkies' – young people with very serious drug habits. As you will see in the book, those few who fall into the dependency trap are almost always people who have suffered some trauma that has not been resolved, or who see no future for themselves. They are people who feel isolated, excluded and marginalised.

That isn't to say there aren't a lot of young people taking drugs. There most certainly are: thousands, millions even. But the vast majority of them are not in trouble with drugs psychologically or physically, and while what they are doing is predominantly illegal, most do not get into trouble with the police. For the most part, they are not dependent and they are not regular long-term users. Most are experimenting with drugs, trying them out, using them recreationally and leaving them behind. There are so few 'junkies' that they barely make it into the statistics. Is that hard to believe? I found it hard to believe because I was under the impression that young people were drowning under a tidal wave of drugs. It's not so.

So how do I know? I'll spare you the headache of staring at piles of statistics wherever I can throughout the book. For the moment, suffice it to say that I have looked at the research on how many young people are taking which drugs, when, how and where. It is absolutely true that a lot more people at a younger age are trying illegal drugs than in previous generations. You might be familiar with the figures. They vary depending on how they were collected, but what they boil down to is that five per cent of eleven to fourteen year-olds have tried drugs, rising to thirty per cent for fourteen to sixteen year-olds. In the twenty to twenty-two age group, sixty per cent have tried illegal drugs, and ninety per cent have been offered them.

That is an awful lot of young people. But pause for a moment – they have *tried* them, or they have been *offered* them. They haven't become the 'gymslip junkies' of the newspaper headline. We too easily make the assumption that trying and being offered drugs turns a kid into a person with a drug habit. Not so. Less than one per cent of people who try drugs are injecting – the method of transmission that is most dangerous; and less than one per cent are using the drugs that tend to cause the most fear – heroin, crack or cocaine. And of those who are, the majority are not teenagers, not experimenters, and not recreational users. They are social, economic and emotional casualties with a pattern of antecedents which makes them vulnerable to many things, drugs being one of them. The slippery slopes and gateways do exist, but people generally don't enter through the gateway marked 'Drug Addiction' nor slide down its slippery slopes unless they already have problems. Drugs do not themselves cause these problems, but the drugs can mask and numb them temporarily.

My attitude to young people and drugs developed after an enormous

Dancing the night away at a rave

amount of research. I began by talking to young people, trying to understand a world I left behind twenty-six years ago. I heard what the young people had to say, I asked them if they took drugs, why they took drugs, what drugs had to offer them. They were helpful, open and honest. Most took drugs because they were fun, they said, and because everyone does, and because it's naughty, and they're curious, or bored. Drugs help you to dance all night, in the case of ecstasy and amphetamine, or mellow out and giggle in the case of cannabis. Some young people took LSD because it was so bizarre and they'd heard it was mind-expanding; they wanted to try out altered states of mind. Cocaine was too expensive, most said, and they would never touch crack or heroin – that was for skagheads and losers. Cool kids don't do crack and heroin.

That was the majority response. Others had a more complex attitude. Taking drugs helped them get over shyness, or was an act of rebellion, or helped to quell anxiety and emotional pain. It helped them to compensate for low self-esteem, it made them part of the gang, it showed they dared too.

Few saw themselves as being in danger. They had seen the horror stories, some had had bad experiences, but they had lived to tell the tale. They did not believe drugs would hurt them: being hurt by drugs was something that happens to other people. If these are common attitudes, which I think they are, we have to be canny about how we do get across the dangers. Kids aren't thick just because they are ignorant.

I asked them what their parents thought, how they reacted, how they'd like them to react. What came out clearly was that they wished they could talk to their parents but most felt they couldn't. They were afraid of the sanctions that would be imposed if they came clean or tried to discuss drugs, they were afraid of disappointing their parents or hurting them, or they were convinced that their parents would no more understand their view of drugs than talk to them in Icelandic.

I also talked to parents, who expressed every shade of emotion and opinion. Some were very frightened of anything to do with drugs and could not discuss them with their children, others were perplexed and confused and didn't know whether to talk to their kids or not, and a few were convinced that they could only protect their children by communicating with them. I have heard of parents who were considering hiring detectives to watch their children and see if they were using drugs, and parents who were thinking of forcing a thirteen year-old daughter to have a blood test to see if she had smoked cannabis. Reactions are very varied. There were others, like the mother who described her instant reaction to a daughter taken to a hospital casualty unit after panicking on ecstasy:

'I didn't know how I'd react, I wasn't prepared for this. Would I be angry – like you are with a four year-old who gets lost in the supermarket and you spank them out of fear when you find them? But when I saw her I just held her close and cuddled her and she cried. I didn't judge her, all that mattered to me was that she should survive and know that whatever she did and whatever happened, I'd be there for her.'

Most of us are somewhere between the blood testing parents and the non-judgemental mother. Most parents lose it when they find out their children are taking drugs – any drugs, any time, in any quantity. It's only natural. They are furious, frightened and frenzied. It wasn't unusual to hear parents of young people in serious drug trouble saying there were times when they wished their son or daughter had died, so devastated were they by what had happened.

But what I discovered from the kids is that this doesn't usually discourage them from taking drugs. It just increases their sense of needing to be surreptitious, so trust breaks down. And revealingly, the parents I spoke to who had children who were on heavy-end drugs and in serious trouble with them physically and psychologically, said that with hindsight anger hadn't helped either them or their children. They all said that what had helped most was to face up to what was happening, to find some help, inform themselves and dig in for a possibly long and probably painful period, during which they would try to help their children to come off drugs.

Nobody pretended it was easy discovering that their child had smoked a bit of cannabis or taken the occasional ecstasy pill at the weekend, or finding them with a needle in their arm. But what they all had in common was the recognition that finding out as much as they could about drugs helped them a lot: they read books, spoke to drugs agency workers and many found it useful to join one of the organisations mentioned in the 'Where to go for help' section at the end of this book – organisations like ADFAM National, a national charity for the families and friends of drug users.

Doing the research for the book I also looked at other sources of expertise apart from the young people themselves and their parents. I read dozens of research papers, pamphlets, government reports and books, largely thanks to the Institute for the Study of Drug Dependence (ISDD) whose library holds the most up-to-date material. This kind of information has provided many lessons, which I hope I have managed to transmit in a readable way throughout the book. I also spoke to people who work in the drugs field: counsellors, nurses and doctors, psychiatrists, policemen, teachers, youth workers and others. Whatever their analysis of why people take drugs, they all agreed on what to say to parents: maintain your line of communication, be prepared to hear what children have to say, learn to listen to them, calm down, get educated. As Sally Murray, a counsellor with twenty years' experience, put it:

'If you go over the top, your child will either withdraw or dismiss what you're saying because you have made no attempt to understand his or her world. We have to show a willingness to see the world through their eyes and remember what it was like for us when we were young.'

Another drugs worker, Colin Cripps, advised parents not to say 'If I ever catch you taking drugs, I'll ...' for the simple reason that the threat will be taken seriously, and if the child in question does need help, he or she will still make sure they won't be caught.

I am not condoning the use of drugs, only trying to understand it and find a path through its controversies and minefields. I am most certainly not saying drugs aren't dangerous: they can be very dangerous.

A question often asked by parents – and an issue that is hotly debated – is at what age one should start to tell children about drugs. I can't answer the question, any more than I would presume to tell anyone at exactly what age we should tell them about sex and contraception. It depends on circumstances, individuals and environment. But it is clear to me that learning about drugs is like learning about any of life's dangers. It's about knowing the dangers, being capable of making decisions wisely, being able to look after yourself. It's the kind of learning that starts in the cradle and goes on throughout life.

The terms 'harm reduction' and 'harm minimisation' were vaguely familiar to me, but I didn't really know what they meant. I do now. They are terms which describe the collective approach of all those involved in making sure our kids are as safe as possible. They are ideas that have taken over from the 'Just Say No' and 'Zero Option' attempts to stop young people taking drugs which don't seem to have worked here or in the United States. Young people have made it abundantly clear that they're not going to just say no. We can tell them to do that until we're blue in the face but they might not take any notice. They may look at us with that patronising patience kids develop as a defence as we rant and rave, or they may slouch off into one of those sulks they specialise in. They may cry, shout, slam out of the house. But it won't stop them taking drugs. Whether we like it or not – and most of us don't – drugs are here to stay.

Harm reduction and minimisation seek to set up a process whereby everyone involved is well informed: users, parents, teachers, club owners, politicians, academics – all of us. It is not even a matter of whether you approve of drug taking or not. It is a matter of common sense. Research shows that many solvent abuse deaths among young people are the result of ignorance, so what is more important? A 'forbidding' campaign, or a campaign of education and information? And just because you point out that the greatest dangers are from putting bags over heads and spraying propellants straight into the mouth, it does not mean you are saying it's OK to do it some other, marginally safer way.

Rock climbing is also a dangerous form of recreation

Some people think that trying to reduce the harm caused by drugs means condoning and even encouraging drug use. But that's like saying that warning teenagers about the dangers of unprotected sex, and telling them about condoms, is just inviting them to go ahead and have sex whether they really want to or not. It's not. Harm reduction says this: if you're going to do something that I can't stop you from doing, at least I can tell you how to minimise the dangers. We have to get away from the assumption that telling someone how to do something dangerous as safely as possible means we are telling them to do it.

Rock climbers learn the ropes or risk their necks. There's obviously a huge difference between showing someone the ropes for rock climbing and introducing the idea of clean needles to a heroin-dependent teenaged son or daughter. The abhorrence levels are different and the cultural assumptions are different. But unless we see it from the common sense point of view, we won't progress.

Perhaps you have read this far and feel offended, angry or insulted. Perhaps you think I'm underestimating the seriousness of some young people's drug experiences. Perhaps you think the harm reduction route is irresponsible. Well, I don't think so. I think the real irresponsibility is ignorance. Perhaps you think my attempt to introduce calm into the furore surrounding young people's drug use is a subversive, undercover attempt to legitimise drug use. Not at all. But it's clear to me after listening to so many children, parents and other experts, that the real danger is in reacting without knowing the story. I hope that this book will help to tell that story.

As you read it you will find that parents and children who have spoken to me have had their names changed and identities disguised. Most wanted this: there is such a stigma attached to being open about drugs that they felt the need to protect themselves. I also approached some of the rock musicians, footballers and others who have been public about their drug experiences hoping that short interviews with them might help parents understand more about drugs. All refused to have anything to do with the project because they did not want any more publicity in relation to their drug use.

There is always something that parents love to hate about youth culture, especially since the invention of the teenager. Nobody would take exception to Elvis Presley's 'hippy-hippy shake' these days – but they did at one time. I come from a generation that grew up at the end of the 1960s and our parents, even the 'hippy-hippy shakers' themselves, were horrified by their teenaged children's cultural habits. Music is always a flashpoint. They would stand white-faced at the bedroom door demanding that we turn down the Rolling Stones or the Grateful Dead, so that they could hear themselves humming along to Elvis. The next lot after me were told to turn down Roxy Music and Led Zeppelin. It's traditional for parents to loathe their children's youth cultures. Those same parents who were teenaged Stones and Roxy Music fans are now telling their kids to turn down the sound of Jungle, Rave, Acid House and Techno.

Every parent is bewildered and many are horrified by the music and the other major aspects of youth culture: the hairstyles, the fashions, the habits, the attitudes. They are most horrified of all by the drugs. But unless we understand the relative attractions of

Elvis once shocked a generation of parents

the elements that make up youth culture, we won't get anywhere with helping our children to be sensible about drugs. They are part of the very fabric of their culture. It's as the MP Paul Flynn told the House of Commons:

'We have opened up a great gulf between our generation and young people. There is as much truth in what we are telling them about drugs as in the myths we and previous generations were told about masturbation and blindness, the tooth fairy and Father Christmas. We are not doing any good in reducing the amount of drugs that they take.'

In this book I have separated the drugs into chapters that reflect their place in youth culture. I have tried to set the drugs story in perspective. Above all, I am trying not to create new myths but to unravel some of the old ones.

Chapter Two

Sniff:

Solvents and volatile substances

Mind-altering sniffing is nothing new. It's a practice that goes back thousands of years to the ancient Greeks, who used inhalants to stimulate mystical or religious ceremonial experiences. In the early nineteenth century in England, ether was popular among people who couldn't afford alcohol. They would sniff it and dance, an early form of raving known as 'ether frolics'. This might sound a bit of a joke, but there's nothing jokey about the use of solvents. The inhalation of vapour from solvents can be extremely dangerous, even fatal. I start with solvents as the first drug of the book, because it's the one younger children experiment with most commonly, along with tobacco and alcohol, and something that most kids grow out of pretty quickly.

What are solvents?

Many products which can be used by sniffers are present in every household. Glue sniffing is the term we are used to, but it isn't only glues that are sniffed. The rest of the products, like aerosol

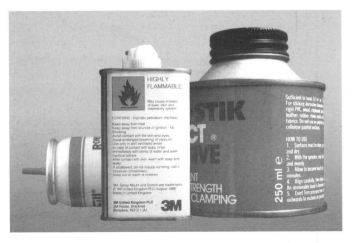

Many products which can be used by sniffers are present in every household

sprays and the propellant gases in them, are referred to as volatile substances. Volatile means that the substance gives off a vapour and evaporates.

Users can get high sniffing the following things:

■ Glues: balsa wood cement, contact adhesives, cycle repair adhesive, PVC cement, adhesive plaster remover and many others

■ Aerosols: air fresheners, deodorants and anti-perspirants, fly spray, hair lacquer

■ Anaesthetics: gas, liquid, local

■ Liquid petroleum gases (LPGs): cigarette lighter refills, butane, propane. These gases are also used as the propellant in most aerosols, having replaced the CFCs which pose a threat to the ozone layer. LPGs are also present in blowtorches and camping gas stoves

■ Commercial dry cleaning and degreasing components

■ Domestic spot removers and dry cleaners

■ Suede cleaner

■ Fire extinguishers: the extinguisher fluid in many extinguishers contains a solvent called halon

■ Petrol

■ Nail varnish and nail varnish remover

■ Paint, paint thinners and paint strippers

■ Typewriter correction fluid.

Who uses solvents?

They are used mostly by younger people, even occasionally by children as young as nine. They are easy to find, cheap and not illegal. Their effects are swift and brief which appeals to children and younger teenagers, who may be more closely observed than older ones.

The Intoxicating Substances Supply Act of 1985 makes it an offence to supply to a young person under eighteen 'a substance which the supplier knows, or has reason to believe, will be used to achieve intoxication'. The law applies to shopkeepers and could also apply to anyone else giving young people such substances. But the law is virtually unenforceable and most of the things kids sniff are found in their homes.

That's the bad news. But expert Richard Ives, who has written extensively about solvents, estimates that although many young people will try sniffing, only a few will go on doing it for any length of time. For most, it's something they try a few times and abandon. The Institute for the Study of Drug Dependence (ISDD) writes in *Drug Misuse in Britain 1996*:

'Solvent misuse is almost exclusively the preserve of young schoolchildren and is generally seen as a passing fad. According to the 1994 British Crime Survey, *although 2 per cent of 16-19 year olds had misused solvents in the last year, no one between the ages of 25 and 44 had, a level of non-use which was unique. Only 1 per cent of 16-19 year olds had misused solvents in the last month, and the only other age group which admitted to such use was the 45-59 year olds and even then, less than 0.5 per cent had, and they could well have been confused by the question.'*

Some surveys show that almost as many girls as boys use solvents, a feature unique to solvents on the drug scene.

A survey of young people by John Balding of Exeter University has found that fewer young people are using solvents now than in the past. This is probably because they have turned instead to LSD and ecstasy, which are increasingly available even to this younger group. Balding thinks that: 'Unlike other drugs studied ... no obvious increase in the use of solvents is predicted.'

Sniffing is not an activity confined to any one area or class of young people. As Richard Ives points out in *Solvents: A Parents Guide*, published by the Department of Health:

'Children from any social class may try sniffing. This does not necessarily mean their parents have failed or brought them up badly. It's more likely to be one of the "disobedient" and sometimes risky things that youngsters do.'

Ives estimates that few children try solvents before the age of eleven. The peak age is around thirteen to fourteen years old.

How are solvents used?

Kids sniff solvents in a variety of ways. Often they transfer gases from their containers to plastic bags or empty crisp packets and inhale them straight into their mouths or noses. Sometimes they put a whole bag over their heads, which is extremely dangerous and can lead to suffocation. They might soak some onto a sleeve and sniff it periodically wherever they happen to be, or carry rags soaked in a solvent. They also spray aerosols into their mouths.

What is the experience of solvents?

The hit is strong and immediate as the solvents enter the blood stream very quickly, but the effects wear off rapidly. The experience is like being very drunk, although sometimes the effect is to make them sick and wretched. A sense of euphoria or unreality – which may be a welcome state of mind – is common. Some people have experiences like those induced by hallucinogenic drugs; for example, they might have delusions and hear and see things which aren't there. There are reports of kids sniffing in groups and having 'group hallucinations' in which they all say they experienced the same delusions. Some people feel dizzy, sick and disorientated. One of the dangers is that sometimes people lose their usual sense of limits and take risks that they wouldn't normally take. But most kids who try sniffing do not get into trouble or have particularly bad experiences.

How can you tell if someone is using solvents?

If kids are really high, it will be obvious that something is up. When they are coming down, or if they are habitual users, they might be moody; but people are often moody during adolescence, so behaviour associated with drug use can equally be associated with growing up. Sniffers tend to smell of the stuff they are sniffing. They may get spots around their mouths and noses, but not all chemicals cause them and spots are also part of growing up. Sniffers may lose their appetites, ask for more money than usual and be evasive about what it's for; they may get frequent headaches and sore throats and lose weight. They may also leave evidence of sniffing: empty containers, crumpled bags, cans or aerosols.

What are the effects of solvents?

While someone is sniffing repeatedly, the 'hangover' effects of pallor, fatigue, forgetfulness and loss of concentration can become a recurring daily pattern. There can be weight loss, depression, tremor and interference with liver and kidney function. All these will normally clear up once sniffing is discontinued.

Persistent and long-term solvent use – over ten years or so – could result in lasting damage to the brain, kidney and liver. Repeated inhalation of petrol can result in lead poisoning. But such damage is rare, as the ISDD reports:

'Lasting damage attributable to solvent misuse seems extremely rare. In Britain, the evidence is limited to a few isolated cases, and surveys of groups of sniffers have not revealed any persistent medical consequences. Temporary impairment is more common.'

How life-threatening is sniffing?

When the solvents craze began around twenty-five years ago, there were only two deaths each year. By 1975 this had risen to nine and by the end of the 1970s it was twenty-one. This figure trebled by 1982 and peaked in 1989 at 151 deaths. Since then it has dropped: in 1994 there were fifty-seven deaths and in 1995 sixty-eight deaths.

In certain cases, sniffing solvents carries immediate physical risks because of the combination of chemicals involved and the methods of taking them. There have been cases of sudden death after the first exposure to solvents and after consistent and repeated use. These sudden deaths fall into two categories: death as a result of the immediate toxic effect of inhaling the substance, which can lead to heart failure or asphyxia; and related deaths, when a sniffer puts a bag over his or her head or has an accident while under the influence.

Until recent years most deaths were due to people putting whole bags full of solvents over their heads. More recently the biggest cause of death has been attributed to spraying chemicals directly into the mouth. As Richard Ives writes:

'Aerosol sprays and butane gas seem to have a special potential to cause harm, particularly when they are sprayed directly into the mouth. This can be very dangerous, not only because aerosols contain substances which may clog up the lungs, but also because aerosols and butane cool the air around them, freezing the throat tissues and possibly leading to swelling and perhaps suffocation. Aerosols and butane can also have a direct effect on the heart muscle, so if sniffing is followed by exertion, death may result.'

Where do kids go to sniff?

Sniffing in groups
Most kids sniff in the company of others. Some sniff in their bedrooms or behind the bike sheds, others do it openly in shopping malls and on street corners where young people gather to lark about. For most, it's a group activity that combines the enjoyment of getting high, being naughty, taking a risk, doing something which makes you feel you have the power to make dangerous decisions, and being one of the gang.

The lone sniffer

Some young people go off and do it alone somewhere secluded or remote like a bus shelter, canal bank, railway line or multi-storey car park. These are often kids in emotional trouble before the sniffing begins, for whom the drug becomes a way of masking emotional pain. They are the exception and not the rule and are also more likely to hit trouble with other drugs.

The danger for lone sniffers is that if they take too much, they can become unconscious. Because they are alone and nobody is there to take them to a doctor or hospital, the consequences can be very serious. In a state of unconsciousness, they might vomit and then choke.

The problem sniffer

Millions of people use drugs with no real problems. The few who get into trouble with drugs are almost always people with major underlying and unaddressed psychological traumas. The sniffing in itself is not the primary problem – it's a manifestation of the need to escape from problems. Lone sniffers and problem drug users are often the people with a suppressed and hidden sadness; and with that often goes low self-esteem, low expectations of themselves and others in relation to them, which can make them shunned by their peers. For them, the chemicals can cause dreaminess, an escape from reality and from a child's anxieties.

A West Midlands study of sniffers found that those who fall foul of the dangers of drugs are young people for whom the future may look bleak, whose family lives are seriously disrupted, who have had some drama or trauma in their lives which hasn't been addressed, who are dangerously bored because of the lack of meaningful activity, and who give in to peer group pressure.

The study noted that:

■ Fifty per cent of the sniffers were from 'broken homes'; they did not understand what was going on between their parents and consequently could not cope with the effects of the emotional fall-out

■ Half said that boredom was a reason for sniffing

■ Many said they were sniffing because of peer group pressure

■ Those of school age often expressed a lack of incentive to work because of poor expectations for their future prospects

■ Seventy per cent reported regular truanting prior to sniffing and thirty per cent reported deterioration in their academic performance since sniffing.

Not all bored kids from deprived areas or so called 'broken homes' are going to become problem sniffers – or sniffers at all. A doctor who studied a group of problem sniffers found that 'Many of them did not live in deprived areas and came from stable, two-parent families'. But those who do become problem sniffers do often have problems at home within the family; and, in the words of the National Children's Bureau, 'rates seem highest for the areas with the most social deprivation'.

It would be unhelpful to pick out any one specific factor as most to blame. The picture is complex. But for parents reading this book and looking for clues as to why kids use solvents, it's worth dwelling on the fact that in the survey mentioned above, fifty per cent of kids in trouble with solvents were from families which were splitting up. It's inevitable that some parents will split up. But it's not inevitable that such splits will damage children. It's more a question of how a split is handled. What emerges from this survey is that the children suffered not only from the split but also from not understanding what was going on.

What can parents do?

Tell me where it hurts

If a child is a secret, troubled sniffer, parents could try to work out what the underlying problems are. Finding out the problems doesn't mean they can be solved. But it's good to let children know you want them to deal with problems in some other way than by sniffing solvents, without being angry with them. Doing this will make them feel less lonely and frightened. In the long term it may help to redress some of the imbalance that made solvents seem attractive to them in the first place.

Tackling their ignorance

Make sure children know the dangers of sniffing. In many of the solvent deaths, the children who died knew very little about what they were doing. By being wise before the event and passing on objective information about drugs, we can help to reduce and minimise the potential harm they can do. This isn't the same as condoning drug use, or encouraging it. It is a recognition that young people use drugs, almost always behind our backs, and that they don't necessarily know what they're doing.

We don't need to exaggerate the dangers, just present them for what they are. It's likely most kids have tried sniffing or know someone who has, and have suffered no ill consequences. Kids aren't stupid but they may be ignorant. We need to get across to them that although their friends may have got away with sniffing solvents, it is a seriously risky business, and of all the drugs most recreational drug users are ever likely to try out, solvents are probably the riskiest.

Obviously we do what we can to discourage kids from doing it at all. But if they are going to persist, we need to tell them these things:

■ Never forget that they and others may have been fine after sniffing, but it is still a very dangerous practice

■ Never do it alone or in remote places

■ Never put bags over their heads

■ Never spray aerosols or butane straight into their mouths

■ Never be afraid to ask for help

■ Never do it because it's easy to find and easy to take: that doesn't make it safe

■ Never light a cigarette or a match or any kind of fire whilst sniffing; there have been cases of fatalities and burns from doing this.

Keeping them calm

Every counsellor and drugs worker will advise parents who discover that their children are using drugs to stay calm. This is easier said than done, but in the case of solvents, it's particularly important not to frighten people when they are under the influence. This is because of the risk – a small one – of what is known as 'sudden sniffing death'. This can happen if someone has directly sprayed one of the more dangerous substances into their mouth: sudden exertion can directly cause muscle spasm in the larynx or the heart and lead to death. It's unusual but it can happen.

The high from solvents does not last more than half an hour, so it's worth waiting until sniffers are coming down before trying to speak to them seriously. While they are high, talk to them soothingly and save the speeches for later when the drug has worn off. If they appear to be losing consciousness or are unconscious, lay them on their side so that if they vomit this won't stop them breathing; make sure there is plenty of fresh air and call an ambulance.

Addressing our own demons

Many of the parents I spoke to while researching this book found that in order to help and understand their children, they needed to confront their own demons. Many said it helped to do this with other people, either with a counsellor, or in a self-help group where there is some anonymity. Family and friends can be too close and judgemental or they add to the distress by their own shocked reactions. (See the list of 'Where to go for help' at the end of this book.)

Attention seeking

If we as parents find evidence of sniffing – used aerosol cans, squeezed-out tubes of glue, paint thinner cans and so on – it's possible the child is trying to tell us something. It may be their way of articulating what they can't say, their way of shocking us into recognising that something is wrong. They might actually want us to know but be too afraid to approach us for help directly. People all too often dismiss such behaviour as 'attention seeking' rather than accepting that the person displaying the need for attention actually really needs it. It's easy to forget how hard it is to articulate what you feel when you're a kid. We need to be in sympathy with them and encourage them to find ways of telling us what they need.

Re-Solv is the society for the prevention of solvent and volatile abuse and can offer help to parents. Their address is 30a High Street, Stone, Staffordshire ST15 8AW, and the telephone number is 01785 817885.

Here is the story of a woman whose son got heavily into sniffing. It says it all: *'I suspected my son was using lighter fuel* but I didn't expect him to confirm this when I asked him. When he did I felt as if I had been punched in the stomach. All I could think of to say to him was: why? He'd always been able to talk to me about things even though ours wasn't the easiest of relationships. I never thought he'd take drugs because he had told me he disapproved of both drugs and smoking. But he said a friend had introduced him to lighter fuel and because it was easy he thought it was safe. And as for why – he said he really enjoyed it.

'I gave him a stiff talking to, thinking this would be an end to it. It wasn't. He sniffed behind his closed bedroom door while I phoned helplines and drugs organisations for advice. I read everything I could about solvents and learned how dangerous my son's habit was. I read that he could be asphyxiated on liquid gas and that I should never have a row and get him excited whilst he was on it as this could trigger a heart attack.

'I rarely managed to keep my cool at the sight of my handsome young son lolling incoherently on his bed. I threw away the keys to his bedroom door and the bathroom door, but he barricaded himself in; I broke down the barricades. We went through a long period in which I alternately pleaded with him to stop, threatened to throw him out, promised him anything he wanted. I reasoned, wept, cold-shouldered, shouted – but nothing made any difference. He would lie, hide the evidence, promise not to take gas when I went out, but still did. There were times when I hated him for the deceit. I would lie awake at night alert for the dreaded sound of hissing gas. I scoured his bedroom every day throwing away anything I didn't like the look of.

'I dared not talk to anyone at his college where he was a student in case they labelled him a junkie. At first I didn't go to our GP for the same reason. Eight months passed and I lost two stone through worry. I was reaching the end of my tether and went to our GP. To my relief he was very understanding and booked us an appointment with a counsellor as a family. Our son reluctantly agreed to come. The counsellor and doctor tried to convince him that inhaling gas was dangerous, but to no avail. We were advised to call an ambulance if he did it. Someone else advised me to hassle my son gently when he was using gas, to go into his room and talk to him, making the experience unrewarding. The idea was he would give up the gas not because he was

submitting to my pressure but because it wouldn't be worth the hassle. It would be his decision to stop, which would give him a way out without losing face. It didn't work, I didn't have the stomach to be that subtle.

'Next time I found him using gas I called an ambulance and he was taken to hopsital with an irregular heartbeat. We told him we'd take him to hospital every time we found him with a bottle of gas. It was then that he decided to stop – it was getting to be too much trouble and fuss. He denied he was addicted but had two very difficult weeks coming off the lighter gas. To our enormous relief he came through. We are very proud of him but it has taken us two years to fully trust him again.'

27

Chapter Three

Puff:

Cannabis

Cannabis has been around for thousands of years and is by far the most popular illegal drug amongst recreational drug users. The surveys tell us that most of the young people who try drugs try cannabis. That doesn't mean it is popular with parents, teachers and others who watch over young people – far from it. It remains a drug we love to hate, perhaps because we are confused about its powers to alter consciousness, cause physical or psychological harm and get people into trouble with the law. The best way to deal with it is to know more about it.

What is cannabis?

Cannabis comes from a plant called *Cannabis sativa* which grows wild like a weed in many countries, hence the street name 'weed'. It has many other street names as well: puff, ganja, dope, shit, pot, grass, sensi, wacky backy, herb, blow, marijuana, hash and others.

Marijuana plant

A joint – a roll-up of cannabis, usually with tobacco

Sometimes it's known by where it comes from: Afghanistan, Lebanon, Morocco, Malawi, Ghana, Jamaica or Pakistan, for example.

There are two common sorts of cannabis: the dried leaves, usually known as grass, and a black or very dark brown resinous residue from the plant compacted down into slightly sticky or dry and crumbly lumps. People smoke cannabis in roll-ups or pipes, cook it in cakes and biscuits and sometimes just eat it. In the UK, it is mostly smoked in 'joints' or 'spliffs' – roll-ups – mixed with tobacco. There is a language that goes with all drugs, and cannabis smokers talk about 'skinning up'; 'skins' is another word for cigarette papers. Cannabis can also be made into oil, a syrupy liquid that can be drunk or smoked after smearing it on cigarette paper, but this method is not often used.

There are more than 400 chemicals in cannabis. The ones that cause people to get 'stoned' are called cannabinoids. The one that has the most effect is called delta9-tetrahydrocannabinol (THC). There are new strains of cannabis being cultivated all over the world, some in Europe, notably in Holland. They are known as skunk, Purple Haze, Sumatran Red and Northern Lights. Cannabis is a class B drug; for more information about what this means, see Chapter six, Drugs and the Law.

Getting stoned: the experience and immediate effects of cannabis

The experience of taking cannabis varies depending on the mood of the user and the type of cannabis used. Someone in an expansive mood might find their mood enhanced, someone feeling withdrawn might find they withdraw even more. The place, the company and the individual all make a difference to the experience.

Many people who like cannabis say that it is fun, it makes them feel mellow and relaxed, time seems to slow down and the senses seem more acute. Some people become very talkative and find everything hilarious, or they are gripped with sudden hunger and get what's known as 'the munchies'. Others find cannabis increases a tendency to become quiet, pacified, even withdrawn. They might find themselves slumped in deep lethargy like couch potatoes.

For some, the drug activates a sense of weirdness so that people, situations and surroundings take on a slightly unreal character. Straightforward situations might suddenly seem bizarre, causing takers to laugh when they probably wouldn't if they weren't stoned.

Caroline, aged seventeen, did a survey at her north London secondary school as part of her statistics coursework for 'A' level:
'In my survey I found that almost half of the seventy-nine seventeen to eighteen year-olds I interviewed had tried cannabis, slightly less than half smoked cigarettes, all had tried alcohol, twenty-one per cent had tried speed, seven per cent ecstasy, thirteen per cent LSD, ten per cent magic mushrooms, twenty-five per cent poppers and one per cent cocaine. There were one or two who wouldn't participate. One deals cannabis, he must have made quite a lot of money because he's got a car with a new sound system and blacked-out windows and he wears smart clothes. He's perfectly all right, his studies are fine. I say he deals cannabis but when I say that I mean it's within the community of his friends, it's not the slippery slope we're always hearing about. Most people get it from their older brothers or their older brothers' friends. The one who said he'd taken cocaine seemed to be showing off — it's debatable if he really did take it.'

Megan, aged thirteen:
'I didn't think cannabis was that nice, it burns your throat, it was the dried leaves sort. I did it because people said it was good, friends my age who had tried it. I would guess at least half my class at school have tried it. I've never seen any at school though, or heard of anyone selling it at school. I've tried alcohol with my dad, and I'm not an alcoholic!'

Dope-induced strangeness can be disconcerting, as one long-term cannabis smoker says: '*There are times when I feel paranoid, nervous, emotional and touchy after getting high on smoking dope.*' And for others, smoking dope can blank out problems and anxieties. On a long-term basis this is not good news because the real problem can get submerged in a cannabis haze – like using alcohol to block out problems and anxieties.

But if paranoia, haze and lethargy were the most common effects of the cannabis experience, it would not remain so popular.

Myths and realities: how harmful is cannabis?

'*The cannabis debate has not been very much concerned with the facts but has been the stage for a fundamental clash of values.*'
Royal College of Psychiatrists report, 1987

The MP Lady Olga Maitland said in the House of Commons in June 1996:

'*Drugs affect the life chances of the young in so many ways. I wish that we could put more effort into warning the young of the health dangers of taking drugs … how many young people realise that cannabis can cause cancer of the mouth and throat, that it can destroy their attention, and that it affects memory? More than that, a young mother can affect her unborn child to a terrifying extent. Her baby could be born with defects.*'

It sounds very frightening. But the truth about cannabis is less frightening, less sensational and more complex.

There is a massive amount of research into cannabis and its effects. The latest and most authoritative documentation is a report from Australia's National Task Force on Cannabis, published in April 1996. At a glance this report also looks pretty worrying. But rather than respond only to the fear it engenders, we need to look carefully at how heavily qualified its findings are. It sums up:

'*The major probable adverse effects appear to be: an increased risk of developing cancers of the aerodigestive tract, an increase in leukemia among offspring exposed while in utero (in the womb), a decline in occupational performance marked by under-achievement in adults in occupations requiring high-level cognitive skills and impaired educational attainment in adolescents, birth defects among children of women who used cannabis during their pregnancies.'*

It looks like bad news for frightened parents and cannabis users – but these are only the *probable* effects on 'chronic, heavy cannabis users', people who smoke a lot of cannabis over a long period of time consistently without a break. Most young people who try cannabis do not take it compulsively in this way and are unlikely to get into trouble physically or psychologically. The same range of results can be found more easily, more conclusively and more often in people who are chronic heavy alcohol or nicotine users.

Smoking cannabis from a water pipe

As you read into the Australian report and its fine print, away from the summary, it emerges that the findings are even more heavily qualified. Let's sort out the myths from the realities.

Birth defects

On the question of cannabis and birth defects, the report says: 'There is suggestive but far from conclusive evidence that cannabis use during pregnancy may have similar adverse effects [as alcohol].' Medical reports always err heavily on the side of caution and it's important to note the phrases 'may have' and 'far from conclusive'. Until such uncertainty is resolved, pregnant women would be well advised to steer clear of cannabis – and alcohol and tobacco as well.

Cancer

The authors of the report say that the issue of whether cannabis causes cancers in the respiratory tract still has to be conclusively investigated. On the general issue of its ability to cause cancer, they note that there is some evidence that 'cannabis smoke is potentially carcinogenic ... probably for the same reasons that cigarette smoke is, rather than because it contains cannabinoids [the compound in cannabis that creates a sensation of being high].' It is probably the inhalation of the burning cannabis that may be damaging.

Most smokers smoke about twenty cigarettes a day, a habitual cannabis user smokes a great deal less. A heavy cannabis smoker is defined by the US National Institute of Drug Abuse as smoking at least two joints daily, but a heavy cigarette smoker smokes forty cigarettes a day.

Some young adults who are heavy cannabis users have been reported with cancers of the aerodigestive tracts, but in the investigative tests many of the people involved were also using alcohol and tobacco. The tests did not conclusively reveal what it was that caused the cancer – alcohol, nicotine or cannabis. Research into this area should be made a priority.

Brain damage

The Australian report looked at the possibility that repeated and heavy use of cannabis could cause brain damage and concluded that the suspicion was based on 'a single poorly controlled study using an outmoded method of investigation which reported that cannabis users had enlarged cerebral ventricles'. This study was widely and uncritically publicised. Other, better-constructed studies have since found no evidence of structural change in the brains of heavy, long-term cannabis users.

In his book *Living with Drugs*, Michael Gossop of the globally respected National Addiction Centre at London's Maudsley Hospital tells the story of a report published in a prestigious medical journal which 'showed' that cannabis causes brain damage. This study was used to justify 'the continuation and strengthening of *every possible measure* to suppress cannabis'. But Gossop

> **Lisa, aged eighteen:**
> '**They used to show off at school** – the boys mostly. They'd say: "I had draw last night, I was well buzzing" – lots of showing off. That dies down. It's accepted that everyone smokes some time or other, so nobody needs to talk about it any more. It's irrelevant. All this talk of heroin addicts – there are hardly any. And the ones there are, we take the piss out of them. There's no status in being a heroin user – we call them skagheads. I feel sorry for them.'

> **Adele Blakebrough, Director of Kaleidoscope, says:** *'A happy, stable person is not going to become chronically drug-dependent. But the child who has no ally is vulnerable. For example, I know of a young boy who was taking his 'A' levels. He was not particularly close to his parents so when they divorced they bought him a flat of his own, and they moved away, leaving him with their dog. He was fine during the term-time, but during the holidays he didn't know what to do with himself and he hung around the local railway station with his dog. A group of kids also hung around there – similarly disaffected – who were already using, and were mostly drug dependent. He got in with them. They welcomed him to their squat and to their parties and because he was lonely and lacked self-esteem, when he smoked cannabis it made him feel socially able and part of that group. He felt valued and supported. His school eventually referred him to us and we became a new temporary ally, and he was all right after seeing us for a while.'*

says that all the patients in the study used other drugs besides cannabis, two were heavy drinkers and the sample did not represent the normal cannabis user: three had mental illnesses, three had histories of head injuries and three had drug abuse histories.

Memory

There is some evidence that memory can be affected by cannabis use. However, in most studies done in laboratory conditions, it emerges that the problems are probably temporary and only affect long-term heavy users. There are no data to show how many long-term heavy users may suffer some impairment to their memories.

Mental illness

There is no evidence that cannabis causes mental illness. But if someone has a predisposition to mental illness, the use of cannabis – and many other drugs – could help to bring it out. Given that so many millions use it, if cannabis did cause mental illness there would be an epidemic of otherwise inexplicable cases. Studies at the University of California at Berkeley in 1968 in the heyday of 'happy hippiedom' illustrate this point: they found that although 10,000 students, at least a quarter of those on the Berkeley campus, had used cannabis, there were no connections between these users and any evidence of mental illness.

Is cannabis demotivating?

Another worry for parents is that cannabis demotivates young people. There is truth in this and even seasoned users and cannabis enthusiasts note its tendency to slow them down. Demotivation can disrupt people's lives. In the case of young cannabis users, it can affect their education and their future. But this is not by any means a regular occurrence; studies show that cannabis is more likely to demotivate the minority of young people who already have problems of low self-worth and do not aspire to succeed at school. For them, cannabis provides a means of masking fears and anxieties and it will do them no favours. The Australian report concludes that because this is a real risk, 'it is desirable to discourage adolescent cannabis use, and especially regular cannabis use'.

Colin Cripps, assistant director of the Network Drugs Advice Project in Newham, London, is concerned about this problem. He says:

'We see young people who have had any motivation taken away by large quantities of cannabis and we see people with periods of short-term mental illness. This is a minority of young users. In ideal circumstances and the right quantities, very few illegal substances do any harm, but there are those who do it in large quantities in circumstances that are not ideal.'

Is cannabis life-threatening?

Some parents believe all drugs to be life threatening. Cannabis, says the Australian Task Force, is not: 'there are no known recorded cases of fatalities attributable to cannabis'.

Is cannabis addictive?

What does addictive mean? In a physical sense it means that a user has built up a tolerance to a drug and needs more and more to achieve the feelings which the drug induces. In a psychological sense, it means that people become dependent on the drug psychologically but not necessarily physically. The word 'addiction' suggests that a person is in trouble because of the drug, that he or she has become an 'addict'. These are very loaded words and imply all kinds of stigmas. For this reason people working in the drugs field – doctors, counsellors and other agency staff – prefer the terms 'dependency' and 'problem drug user' or 'dependent drug user'.

The issue of whether cannabis is 'addictive' or not is still controversial. The body cannot become physically dependent on

Dinah, aged eighteen: 'I had my first contact with drugs at thirteen. It was like, let's be naughty and have some marijuana. You grow out of that "let's be naughty" thing pretty quickly. I didn't feel very well but I quite liked it. It made me feel happy and it made me feel like eating. It made me feel mellow, just sitting around giggling. I think I felt ill partly because I felt guilty. I didn't go home while I was stoned. I did it occasionally when we had some money and were short of ideas for what to do, but I never got into any trouble and certainly don't much care whether I have any or not. It's just now and again. No big deal.'

it, as it does with nicotine or opiates, but users can end up using it compulsively. The Australian report finds:

'While acknowledging the existence of the syndrome [cannabis dependence], we should avoid exaggerating its prevalence and the severity of its adverse effects on individuals. Better research on the experience of long-term cannabis users should provide more precise estimates of the risk.'

Time and again, studies show that dependence hits people whose hope and potential are compromised. Those most likely to get into trouble with any drugs, including cannabis, are likely to be already suffering from unaddressed anxieties, to be eager for an escape before they even use the drug.

Chief Superintendent Bill Wilson of Kingston-upon-Thames Constabulary says:

'Nowadays, on some estates you see kids with no hope, no hope of a job. The education system has let them down and they drift into a depression, they're demotivated, there's nothing for them in life. Some get into trouble – they get into crime to feed their habits, and the habits could just as easily be scratch cards, gambling, lottery tickets, or fruit machines as drugs. People always think it's drugs they're using because drugs are easily identifiable and they think other things don't create a psychological or physical dependence. But in the end, most of the thirteen to sixteen year-olds who experiment with cannabis are nice, hard-working kids.'

Tom is fifteen. He is one of the typical young people Bill Wilson is talking about. Tom smokes cannabis now and again and says he experiences no side effects. He has this to say:

'I think part of the problem with parents is that they don't make a distinction between drugs. There's a big difference between the odd joint and crack or heroin. Cannabis isn't addictive, although people who enjoy it do it more, but it's not like smoking cigarettes, you don't have to have one every hour.'

Is cannabis a 'gateway drug'?

Many people believe that cannabis is what is popularly known as a 'gateway drug', one that leads people on to other more dangerous drugs and ultimately to the one parents fear most: heroin. If it were

Joan: *'**Cannabis is a bad, wicked waste of money** and I dread to think what it does to your insides. I suspect it's damaging, but then so is alcohol and with alcohol it's a question of moderation. I wouldn't allow cannabis in the house because it's illegal and the smell is disgusting. I know friends who make the cookies but I've never been tempted to try. I'd rather have a glass of wine. If I found my daughter was trying it, I probably would be very angry. I'd go through it with her like we did with cigarettes, but I can't be on their backs all the time. I can't walk around behind them. To be honest it just scares me to think about it and all the kids are using it.'*

true that cannabis smokers went on to heroin, writes drugs expert Ross Comber, 'there would be many more heroin users given the millions who have tried cannabis, perhaps eight million in the UK alone'. It's like saying: 'Oh my God, my fourteen year-old has had a half of lager, in no time he will be swallowing a bottle of bourbon a day ...'. The number of heroin users remains very small, especially when compared to the number of people using cannabis. It is true that heroin users also smoke cannabis – but not that cannabis smokers also use heroin.

Young people enjoying a drink: is the occasional 'joint' any more dangerous?

But there is a way in which cannabis is a gateway drug. Gina, a long-term cannabis user now aged forty-six and with a grown-up son, explains:

'You could see cannabis as a gateway drug because if young people are convinced by adults that it is an awful thing, that it is destructive and addictive, they may well say after using it for a while, well, this isn't doing me any harm so the adults are probably wrong about the other drugs – they just want to stop me having fun. If they've been lied to about cannabis, then the adult world could be lying about the rest of them. Then they might try dangerous drugs like crack, cocaine or even heroin, because they think if cannabis hasn't hurt me or hooked me, and the adults told me it would, nor will the others.'

Why do kids take cannabis?

For some young people, taking cannabis is the thing you do with your friends, and you do it because they do it. Tanya, now in her thirties, remembers why she first tried cannabis:

'I first used dope when I was eighteen because everybody was smoking. I did it because everybody else did. Somehow I had the idea I'd get a different experience, get onto another level. It was the style at the time to be as laid-back as possible, it was part of being cool. Perhaps it was because we were young and insecure and paranoid about saying something the others would think was stupid.'

Times haven't changed much. As 17 year-old Kate says:

'I think young people use cannabis because it's a social thing, like drinking, it's a different sensation. I've tried it, I'm not a huge fan, I just do it occasionally. It mellows me out.'

To add to its unpopular public image, cannabis is part of the fabric of teenage rebellion. For many kids, rebelling is a stage on the

Dave, a former musician with a successful rock band, is a long-term cannabis smoker:
'We had to hide the fact that I smoke it from our children, because when my elder daughter Sally was at primary school, she said something about her daddy putting something in cigarettes. The teacher advised us to be careful, because if the wrong person heard this it could make a lot of trouble. So I had to do it in secrecy and hide my stash somewhere in the house they wouldn't look – it was a sort of role reversal. It only came out of the closet recently because they heard someone asking me to roll a joint. They are very sensitive. A friend had recently died from a drugs-related death, so their sense of danger and drugs was heightened. So the revelation that their dad smokes marijuana they associated with death, they thought I'd die. At school they had been told drugs are bad, full stop. I suppose school has to say that.

'My younger daughter wasn't too bad, she's ten, but the older one, she's thirteen, was absolutely distraught and took a whole night to comfort. She thought I was in mortal danger, that I was doing something terribly wrong, and she knew I'd betrayed her in some way. I still don't smoke joints in front of her and I wouldn't like my kids to do it. That makes me a hypocrite. I think you have to say they'll probably experiment and so let's talk about it. I'd hate to create an atmosphere in which my kids had to sneak behind my back. I'm glad that at this stage they are both very anti-drugs and sound like people who never want to take any at all.'

route from childhood to adulthood. Smoking cannabis might signal the same breakthrough from childhood into independence as staying out late, running up the telephone bill, playing loud music in the bedroom or having sex.

Cannabis is naughty, naughty is cool. Penny, aged thirteen, says:

'Kids smoke dope because it's naughty. I know kids who smoke because they think it's cool. They say, "If my mum caught me she'd kill me!" I think it's like grown-ups having affairs, sneaking away from their wives and their husbands.'

Cannabis has a reputation among young people for being fun. It offers the attraction of a reasonably cheap good time. Add the hint of rebellion, and it's an obvious adolescent prank to smoke dope.

Cannabis also represents a challenge and even a threat to those whose prime aim is to maintain society's status quo. There are many young people who seek to challenge authority. As Terrence McKenna, author of *Food for the Gods*, writes:

'[Cannabis] has a mitigating effect on competition, causes one to question authority, and reinforces the notion of the merely relative importance of social values.'

There is also the attraction of risk-taking, which is a normal part of adolescence. In the case of drugs, the attraction is compounded by their illegal status. In January 1997, Paul Flynn MP said in the House of Commons:

'We would say to our young people, "Say no to any chemical product; say no to those drugs", but have we forgotten what we felt when we were fifteen or eighteen? All young people know that they are immortal – as did we when we were young. Others may die, but they will not. They are risk takers – that is part of being young. Saying no to them is often a perverse incentive for them to take such products.'

Part of becoming independent is being allowed, within reason, to make your own decisions and risk making your own mistakes.

Some people say that cannabis enables them to take a holiday from themselves, to escape from routine and intensify their experience of being alive. Julia, a woman in her forties, comments:

'This intensity isn't something I could have articulated as a teenager, but it's what I remember about cannabis although I have rarely used it since I was very young. It's a sense that even the

Georgia, aged twelve: *'**We all have to breathe in nicotine**, it's gicky and nasty, I don't know why people don't make more of a fuss about cigarettes. Loads of people smoke cigarettes but you don't see them with a spliff, do you? And you see thousands of people in pubs and most of my friends have tried alcohol, they've had a sip of wine with their parents. I have. But if anyone mentions dope they say: "Oh my God!".'*

most minor passing details are interesting, that conversations are meaningful and silence comfortable, it creates a sense of everything being fascinating. I expect the conversations were rubbish but it didn't matter.'

For some it seems to offer comfort in a difficult world. Not being able to feel comfortable in the world is also to do with the state of one's self-esteem. As the agony aunt for *Just Seventeen* magazine, I used to get 12,000 letters a year from teenagers. Most were at heart about lack of self-confidence and the fears and problems related to lack of self-esteem. What I saw between the lines of the stories about heartbreak, bullying, verbal and sexual abuse, the falling-out with friends, the frustration with parental limits and so on, was a crisis in self-esteem among adolescents.

For a minority, cannabis use goes one stage further and becomes a problematic and habitual way of dulling the pain of unaddressed trauma. Sally Murray, a drugs counsellor with twenty years' experience, says:

'Very few kids get into problems because of cannabis. But having said that, I do see them. Most are trying to blot out a problem, something unpleasant in their lives. They can't get up until they've had a spliff and then they smoke all day. Cannabis has lost its initial joy for them and it's just become a tool to keep reality at bay. It masks fear of the future, the sense that there are no prospects of jobs, no hopes, no dreams. It also masks traumas, it makes reality duller but easier to take. They usually have problems

at school. But the drug is a symptom and not the cause of their malaise, that's the key to understanding them. It goes right across the social spectrum as well. There are kids from very high-achieving professional families for whom the pressure to achieve becomes terrifying and paralyses them. And of course there are those kids who have suffered some kind of family trauma, with nobody stopping to think what the child's perception of this huge event in their lives was.'

What can parents do?

Don't panic

Get cannabis in perspective – which doesn't mean the same as condoning its use among teenagers. We have to know what they see in it and be fully informed about any statement we make, in order to try to stop them getting into cannabis smoking.

Parents might find it comforting to take note of a point made by the Australian study: 'In the majority of cases cannabis use is experimental ... most users use the drug on a small number of occasions, and either discontinue their use, or use intermittently.' As Jenny, aged nineteen, says:

Naomi, the 44 year-old mother of a son with what she sees as a cannabis problem, has been through every aspect of a parent's experience in her reactions to her son: *'My son Johnny, who is twenty-five now, is a drug addict. He smokes cannabis. I first noticed when he was fifteen, which was also when he left school. You never think it will happen to your son. I went ape. I went to his bedroom and saw a bag of it. It was the first time I'd ever seen it, brown stuff in a bag. Johnny was always a difficult child. He was a slow learner, and looking back I think he had a problem at school which was never picked up. I should imagine I walloped Johnny. You block out the memories, they're too painful, but yes, I hit him and threw things at him. It wasn't the right thing to do. Sometimes you hate your son, you wish he was dead, you wish you'd never had him.*

'My husband went ape as well. My husband is part of the problem. He has spoiled the boys materially, with money but not with love – he doesn't know the meaning of love and what it means to a child. He has his rules and lives by them, and if you don't live by them you're weak, you're not normal. My husband has always reacted to Johnny violently. Johnny's problem is that he has low self-esteem as a result of being a slow learner. I've tried to get him to talk about drugs, I've pinned him into his bedroom, I've said: "I'll never leave, I'll always be by your side". It's new for me to be able to communicate with him about drugs. It's since I went to Families Anonymous, and a whole new world of revelation is opened up to me. For the past few months he's been working with my husband at the shoe shop. He's a fantastic worker.

'Johnny says he has no problem, he says I have the problem. I wonder if he's right. Going to FA has opened my eyes. I didn't realise love is not enough, you have to listen, to focus. Being at home for your child, reading them stories at night, going to parents' meetings – there's so much more to it than that. You have to open your mind. I was in denial for twenty-six years. I didn't realise what was happening to me was also happening in some way to him. I was an abused wife, my husband was violent. I was battered. Fifteen years ago he beat me up really badly. The kids saw everything. Now I've met other parents and I have to begin to admit to myself that Johnny's drug addiction could have something to do with us.'

'I hardly ever have cannabis nowadays, although when I was younger I tried it a few times for a laugh. Most of my friends are the same as me, only a very few take it often, real dopeheads are rare.'

Putting cannabis in the same category as almost any other illegal drug only adds to the anxiety parents feel. It is not like solvents, LSD or ecstasy: it does not carry the same physical or psychological dangers as these drugs and it bears no resemblance to amphetamine, cocaine or opiates like heroin. Cannabis has a bad name because it is an illegal drug and illegal means criminal, and in a few cases it can cause problems.

However hard it is, the calmer we are, the more attention young people will pay to what we say, even if they make a display of indifference. It's a very difficult balance to achieve, especially when parents wish they could control and forbid the consumption of an illegal drug. But there's no guarantee that anything we do, whether extreme or mild, will prevent young people experimenting with cannabis. It's all around them, they are almost bound to come into contact with it.

Discuss the subject
The best approach is reasonable discussion. The more unreasonable parents seem to their children, the more intense the childrens' desire to prove independence by breaking the rules. This is what one mother, aged fifty, found:

Gina: 'I wouldn't have wanted my son to get into cannabis as a release from problems, or to forget things. But I wouldn't have minded him using it for recreation at weekends from about the age of fourteen. I'd only have minded him smoking it if it was for a reason other than to have fun.'

'My son was about fifteen. One day he and some friends were caught with cannabis. I thought it would lead to something else and he would die. I didn't know anything about drugs, all I knew was from stories in newspapers about people dying. My husband and I thought if we told him how dangerous cannabis was, he wouldn't smoke it. I felt fear more than anger. When we started talking to him he said, what made us think he was doing it?

'After that I searched his room regularly because he behaved strangely – he was always rushing out, the phone rang for him all the time, he had all these new friends. I didn't want my son seeing them. His old friends stopped calling round. I started listening in to his calls and saying: "Get off that phone!". I thought I was doing the right thing but I was wrong. The right thing was to learn more about drugs and talk to him but I was crying all the time.'

Communicate

The picture changes if parents are convinced that their children are badly affected by cannabis because they bunk off school, sleep too much and generally show a lack of motivation to do anything except slouch on a long-term basis. If that is their approach to life, it's probably going to be hard to get through to them.

Penny, aged thirteen:
'I haven't had cannabis, but I want to. A lot of people I know have, most of the boys in my class at school mouth off about it. They say they're going to parties where you pay a fiver to get in and then you get some cannabis. They said it was excellent, I don't think they really did it. The boys say: "I'm going to get high and me and my girlfriend blah blah …". It's not just drugs they brag about, it's sex as well. They say: "I've got the leg over this girl and had cannabis." But most of the boys are frigid, it's all talk.'

This could be a temporary state of affairs, something they go through for no underlying serious reason. But adolescent stroppiness is often a mask for something else, some anxiety of their own which they haven't told us about. Their refusal to communicate with us could arise because of some old and embedded fear they have of displeasing or upsetting us. We know or suspect they are smoking cannabis and identify it as the cause, but other things could in reality be at the heart of the matter. So rather than starting with the cannabis, we can try another way into helping them.

Sally Murray comes across this kind of situation during counselling sessions with parents:

'We have to let them know we won't reject them, that they are our children and even when we want to throttle them, they come first. Adolescents are difficult, they are bolshy, they have mood swings, they behave unpredictably, but I have often said to parents: "Catch your child being good even if you have to contrive a way to do that, give them some positive feedback, not always negative." I've seen parents returning to me after trying this approach which has helped them.'

Sally Murray has also known parents whose instinct was to report their children to the police. Ann, a thirty-seven year-old mother, said:

'Cannabis – that's marijuana, isn't it? Young people use it and they're all in danger of becoming junkies. I'd definitely ban it. If necessary I'd call the police in on them if any child of mine tried that awful stuff.'

This is not something that Sally Murray recommends:

'Some parents who find their children smoking cannabis to

James, aged seventeen: 'I started puffing when I was nine because of older kids. Why? God knows – because everyone else was. I liked it. It was wicked. It felt good. It gave us superiority because it was drugs, and dangerous. I wouldn't say it affected my school work but it affected my homework because I didn't do any. Then I got caught and the headmaster rang my dad in front of me, I was suspended. My dad was more upset than angry, he was lost, he didn't know what to do, he was a nervous wreck. I think it would have been better if he'd sat down and spoken to me about it all rather than blanking it out. I don't think he ever talked to me. After they suspended me, I was actually expelled. I was very depressed. My mum said she was very

disappointed in me and asked me for the names of the kids who gave it to me. I gave her one name and the youth and community people got hold of him and he hasn't spoken to me since. I lost a lot of friends. They moved to get me out of the area.

'In the new area someone asked me if I could get some puff. I said I could. Of course I couldn't, but I was bragging, being the big guy. I started hanging around with that boy. We started nicking car radios, we did ten or fifteen cars of a night and never got caught. Then my mum found stereos under the settee. She went mad big-time, freaked out. I came in and the stereo's on the table and mum and dad are sitting there, and they shouted at me for an hour. At that time, I couldn't see my parents as humans

with feelings. You only realise that later. You don't believe you have the power to hurt their feelings, they're like robots, you're there, they're there, you do your own thing, they do their own thing. It was only later that my mum said tell me the truth – it'll be better for you. That works.

'I puffed in my bedroom. My parents were upset and depressed about it, but I couldn't stop. They said it was better I did it in my own bedroom than on the street. I loved it, it was like yeah man, cup of tea, spliff, I'm skagged out, feels wicked, like being wrapped in a warm quilt, nothing can harm you. There's definitely something I'm trying to get away from, but I don't know what it is. I get money fitting central heating, £30 a day.

extremes want to go to the police. For example, they discover the kid's money from their savings account is all gone or they have been stealing from their parents. But if they go to the police, that means their channels of communication with their children are damaged forever. I always say: "For God's sake, clear the debt any way you can rather than go to the police." Of course there must be sanctions, but that isn't a helpful one. So if a young person has such a big problem with cannabis, before you start trying to punish them, you have to work out what led them to use the cannabis as a means of blocking out their days. And sadly, with a serious cannabis habit – it's psychologically addictive but not physically – kids shouldn't be waking up and wanting to block out every day. Every day should be good for them. You have to ask yourself what the hell has gone wrong.'

Sarah, aged thirteen says:

'My friend's parents said they were going to take her to the doctor for a blood test to see if she had been smoking cannabis. I think that's terrible.'

Cannabis shows up in the blood for about a week if only used occasionally and up to five weeks if used chronically and habitually. But the idea that any parents would force a child to have blood taken to ascertain the presence or absence of cannabis is alarming. During the research for this book, I rarely came across such extreme reactions. But where parents might feel rage or panic, they would be well advised to think carefully before saying anything like this to their children. If they did suggest such a thing, it is doubtful that their children would ever forget and what trust there is between them would be threatened.

Keep cool

Most parents who discover that their children are trying cannabis feel angry and nobody can say categorically that expressing that anger is always a bad thing. But many of the parents I spoke to said they were very angry at first and regretted it later. Sally Murray has noticed when counselling young people for whom drugs have been a problem, that fear of their parents' anger can be a block to their recovery:

'As adults, we forget how frightening we are to our children when we're angry. We are their gods, we are physically huge as they grow up and it takes a long time to stop seeing your parents as these god-like creatures.'

---

*I smoke puff every day. I spend £45 a week on it. I have five joints a day to myself and the rest I share with my mates. I didn't want sex, and girls are the last thing on your mind. I just wanted to talk to my mates. It's not like lager, that makes you shout. We're as tame as anything. No such thing as a cannabis lout! I'd like to stop because it makes me slightly paranoid and my memory isn't good. I can't get up in the mornings, and life is flying past. I can't remember whole patches of my life. I've also done about 150 ecstasy tablets and a bit of coke. I'd never touch heroin. I don't know what stops me from stopping. Every day we say we're going to stop but the temptation's always there. I won't be smoking when I'm an adult. God knows when that will be.'

Empathise

Sally Murray sees some young people for whom cannabis has become a problem. She has noticed a recurring feature:

'Children often feel responsible for things that happen, when of course we know they're not; but we tend to forget that they blame themselves. It's important to tell them that if, for example, parents are splitting up, or even just getting on badly, it's not their fault. Children internalise that kind of anxiety, and it catches up with them later. Cannabis is easily available to younger children and offers them a chance to relax and mellow out, to forget their anxieties, and then when it becomes a problem they are using it to block everything out. We need to focus on our kids, to empathise, to remember how we perceived the world as children.'

Get help

One of the worst things when you are a scared parent is to feel isolated. There will always be someone who can advise and help you. Counsellors at the National Drugs Helpline on 0800 776600, which operates twenty-four hours a day, can advise, comfort and talk. They can also pass on contact numbers and addresses for drugs agencies in the relevant area. Any shame parents might feel about admitting their children take drugs is quickly dispelled when you remember that you are in the company of other parents, because more kids try drugs now.

Kate, aged seventeen:
'My parents have always been on about drugs since I was twelve. They smoke cannabis, my father more than my mother. I don't know when I realised it was drugs, I just used to see my dad and his friend rolling up cigarettes with brown stuff crumbled into them. I don't have any desire to take drugs. It's partly because of the way I was brought up – they hold no mystery for me.'*

Drugs information at Hackney Library, London

A brief history of cannabis

Looking at the history of cannabis helps us to understand the strong reactions against it. Cannabis has a long history, dating back to 2727 BC, when it appeared in a Chinese compendium for medicines. For centuries it was known as hemp and used to make textiles; the word 'canvas' may have derived from the original Greek name, *kannabis*. The United States President George Washington grew it in his garden and used the female plants for his private 'medicinal' use. It was popular with smart Manhattan ladies in the earlier part of this century.

Cannabis began to achieve notoriety when Mexican immigrants, brought into the United States to do jobs the Americans didn't want to do, brought their cannabis-smoking habits with them. With the onset of the Depression in the 1930s came a wave of racist reaction against the Mexicans, who were economically expendable. With this came the backlash against cannabis as something associated with those the authorities sought to condemn, in order to justify herding them back to Mexico. By then, cannabis was popular with jazz musicians, actresses and artists – people seen in 1930s, 40s and 50s America as subversive types who threatened

George Washington grew cannabis in his garden for 'medicinal use'

the status quo. The war on drugs had begun and cannabis smokers found themselves outlawed unless prescribed the drug by doctors. (Birdseed sellers were up in arms at the thought of a ban because it made their canaries sing, so they too were exempt.) Soon after, cannabis was dropped as a registered medicine. By the 1960s, when radicals were shaking the fabric of American society and declaring themselves to be dope smokers, the national demonisation of cannabis really took off, moving across the Atlantic shortly afterwards.

In 1950s Britain, cannabis was seen as a dangerously sexy drug used by West Indians who had arrived to do the jobs whites didn't want. They brought cannabis with them, as much part of their culture as the travelling businessman's bottle of duty-free whisky. A barrister wrote about it in 1952, after being told by police that the cannabis peddlers were 'the most evil men who have ever taken to the vice business'. By way of illustrating this, the barrister went to a bebop club where he was shocked to find:

'... twenty-eight coloured men and some thirty white girls, none of the girls looked more than twenty-five. Girls and coloured partners danced with an abandon – a savagery almost – which was both fascinating and embarrassing. I had seen my first bebop club, its coloured peddlers, its half-crazed, uncaring girls.'

One wonders what the 1952 barrister would have made of the 1990s rave scene. Looked at from a social perspective, the taboo is more to do with cannabis as a threat to authority and white supremacy, a flag of rebellion, than as a truly dangerous substance. It helps to know where the prejudice against it started – a prejudice that would have attached itself as strongly to alcohol if that had been the drug the Mexicans in the United States or the West Indians in the United Kingdom had brought with them as a substance little known to the indigenous population.

Jeannie, aged thirteen: *'My mum and dad caught me drinking alcohol and smoking with my friends in the park. They said if I did either things again, they'd withdraw my pocket money. I did smoke again and they explained how bad it is for your health, and they stopped my pocket money. They're not especially strict, and I suppose I'd rather they told me not to, really. I've got a friend whose parents let her stay out until midnight on Saturdays and Sundays, and I really envy her. I'm not allowed out after ten thirty and always have to be with a friend, but she doesn't. I suppose I do see my mum and dad's point of view, at least it means they care. And they're not silly about it, they don't come over all strict and bossy, they're just like, you've got the rest of your life to stay out late and smoke cigarettes, but while we're protecting you for the next three years or so, we want you to be safe and healthy. Thirteen year-old girls out at midnight aren't safe.'*

Megan, aged thirteen:
'My mum used to smoke a lot of dope in front of us because she had cancer. She did it for the pain, and when it stopped working she stopped doing it. She made a joke of it, but it worried her. It does good things as well, it's not all junkie, horrible nastiness and yet it's still illegal, even for use like that. If people want to smoke it, why stop them? It's like skiing – nobody stops you doing that, even though you could kill yourself. People say cannabis is the only safe drug, but it's illegal, so they drink their lives away instead of getting pleasure from something that doesn't harm you. I'm glad my mum used it. It helped her before she died.'

The prejudice against cannabis has survived despite repeated findings of its relative safety by eminent bodies going back over more than one hundred years. A brief run through some of the major and highly respected reports shows similar conclusions to those of the Australian Task Force in 1996:

■ In 1894, the Indian Hemp Drugs Commission reported its findings to the British government: 'The evidence shows moderate use of ganja or charas [cannabis] not to be appreciably harmful, while in the case of moderate bhang [a cannabis drink] drinking, the evidence shows the habit to be quite harmless.'

■ The La Guardia Committee, New York 1944, put together by thirty-one eminent professionals, concluded that cannabis was not addictive, did not lead to use of 'harder' drugs such as morphine or cocaine and did not affect personality or cause crime or juvenile delinquency

■ The Wootton Committee, set up in 1968 to advise the British Government, found that 'the long-term consumption of cannabis in moderate doses has no harmful effects.'

■ The Shafer Report, set up by President Nixon in the United States in 1972, found that there is no reliable evidence that cannabis causes genetic defects or brain damage, the physical effects of cannabis are of little significance, it causes no psychological deterioration, it does not result in physical dependence, and 'the overwhelming majority' of users do not go on to use other drugs.

■ The Le Dain Report, Canada 1972, came to the same conclusions as these other investigations and concluded: 'It is a grave error to indulge in deliberate distortion or exaggeration concerning the alleged dangers of a particular drug, or to base a programme of drug education upon a strategy of fear. It is no use playing "chicken" with young people; in nine cases out of ten they will accept the challenge.'

Prohibition of cannabis

The process of prohibition started in 1923 when the South African government proposed to the League of Nations that it should be subject to international regulation as an addictive drug. The concern arose from mine-owners' suspicions that their African workers were slacking, which they chose to attribute to cannabis consumption. The war against cannabis continued at an international policy-making level a year later, at a conference on opium in 1924 during which the Egyptian delegate said cannabis was the main cause of madness in Egypt. The British banned it in 1928 for non-medicinal use, but doctors could prescribe it until 1973, although in practice not many did. There is no evidence that cannabis causes insanity but it was duly put under strict new controls, to which the British agreed. It remains on the list of Class B drugs, along with barbiturates, much stronger and potentially more dangerous drugs.

Medicinal use of cannabis

Legal medicinal use of cannabis in Britain dates back to the mid-nineteenth century, when it was used to cure migraine, gout, tetanus, convulsions, depression and delirium tremens. Queen Victoria's doctor said of cannabis that it was 'one of the most valuable medicines we possess'. After 1973, it was taken off the prescription list in Britain and replaced by anti-depressants and tranquillisers. Even the most needy cannabis users were instantly criminalised, including severe arthritis sufferers, many of whom find that over-the-counter prescription painkillers have undesirable side effects.

A survey carried out by the British Medical Association (BMA) in 1994 found that seventy-four per cent of doctors would prescribe cannabis if it were legal. After their annual representative meeting in July 1977, the BMA announced: 'This representative body believes that certain additional cannabinoids should be legalised for wider medicinal use'. In certain states in the United States, cannabis is now legal if prescribed by doctors for certain illnesses. The Australian report referred to earlier in the chapter found that there was 'reasonable evidence' that one of cannabis' chemical constituents, delta9-tetrahydrocannabinol, known for convenience as THC, is effective for cancer patients whose chemotherapy drugs make them feel sick. The report noted that:

An advertisement in the Illustrated London News, 1887

Queen Victoria's doctor said of cannabis: 'It is one of the most valuable medicines we possess.'

'... there is probably sufficient evidence to justify THC being made available in synthetic form to cancer patients whose nausea has proved resistant to conventional treatment. There is also reasonable evidence for the potential efficacy of THC and marijuana in the treatment of glaucoma.'

Support for cannabis as a medicinal drug came from an unlikely quarter in 1986, when a United States judge declared after hearing masses of evidence from the US Drug Enforcement Agency:

'Nearly all medicines have toxic, potentially lethal effects, but marijuana is not such a substance. In its natural form it is one of the safest substances known to man. By any measure of rational analysis, marijuana can be safely used within a supervised routine of medical care.'

There is also evidence that cannabis could be effective in the treatment of asthma as well as in the management of pain. The Australian report points out that the reason why there hasn't been enough research into this area of possible use, is because of the 'unreasonable fear' that using it for medicinal therapy would send mixed messages to young people.

Should cannabis be legalised?

The debate over whether or not cannabis should be legalised continues. Here are some of the principal points made by both sides.

Arguments against legalising cannabis

'We must resist in all possible manner any attempt to legalise soft drugs, as that is the start of the slippery slope to crime and a deprived life.'
Robert Spink MP, March 1994

If we legalised cannabis – and some would argue we should go further and legalise cocaine, heroin, crack and LSD – it would encourage people to regard it as safe. Many more people would immediately start taking these drugs and become dependent. Legalisation would encourage not only their use, but their abuse.

Although it isn't possible to say for certain what would happen if cannabis were legalised, if we take alcohol as an example of a drug that is available and legal, there would be mass consumption of cannabis with all the possible problems and complications that would bring. All drugs carry some kind of risk, some more than others. Things are bad enough in relation to nicotine and alcohol, so why legalise another potentially troublesome drug?

Most policy makers have argued that it is not feasible or thinkable to legalise any drug. Michael Howard summed up this position when he said as Home Secretary in June 1994:

If cigarettes were invented now, would they be made illegal?

Some say alcohol is bad enough, so why legalise another troublesome drug?

'... they [drugs] destroy the very fabric on which our society rests. With legalisation, the number of young people addicted to all kinds of drugs would be likely to increase.'

Legalising cannabis and any other illicit drug will greatly increase the availability of drugs and encourage their use, and therefore abuse. Criminality would not be reduced with legalisation:

'Even if, heaven forbid, the authorities sold and taxed drugs, organised crime would undercut the price, intimidate and distort the market, while still controlling production.'
Graham Saltmarsh, National Criminal Intelligence Service, October 1993

If we decriminalise those who buy and sell cannabis, we are saying cannabis is safe enough for people to buy in the same way as alcohol and nicotine. But if the adult world gives this message to young people, they will think that it is all right to use cannabis and they will be more vulnerable to some of the problems associated with it.

Arguments for legalising cannabis

'No study has shown that cannabis use leads to dependency on hard drugs ... if it were decriminalised, we would immediately remove the unnecessary 42,000 convictions a year for cannabis use and end the five-fold increase in cautions.'
Alan Simpson MP

The enormous increase in drugs offences committed by those under twenty-one are mostly cannabis related. Cannabis features in ninety per cent of all drug offences.

'Anthropological studies and historical reviews suggest that abundant supply does not inevitably result in uncontrolled consumption.'
Philip Robson, psychiatrist, lecturer and author, in his book *Forbidden Drugs* (1994)

'If cigarettes and alcohol were invented now, they would be illegal – they are probably more dangerous than the softer end of the cannabis scene.'
Chief Superintendent Bill Wilson, 1996

In March 1994, Tony Banks MP advocated a new D class of drugs, which would put cannabis on a similar basis as alcohol and nicotine, regulating its sale and use:

'If one was being strictly logical, one would consider the health aspects of cannabis and ban alcohol and nicotine. I have not been able to discover anyone who has died from using cannabis, but every year, tens of thousands die from illnesses related to alcohol and nicotine ... [which] are far more potent drugs than cannabis ... the debate involves not only 1960s hippies, but judges, senior police officers involved with the drugs squad, the head of Interpol [and] the Surgeon General of the USA. [Legalisation] would: release law enforcement resources; improve police-community relations and police effectiveness; eliminate crime to fund illegal purchases; improve the health of people using drugs ... improve early access to treatment for those developing drugs problems. The legal trade would have tax benefits and eliminate the excessive illicit profits that generate violence and corruption ...'

Most people regulate their intake of dangerous substances. Cannabis is easily available and not expensive. Most people who try it don't go on to be problematic users.

Prohibition does not stop illegal trading in substances people enjoy. During prohibition of alcohol in the United States, thousands died after drinking crude bootleg liquor and fortunes were made by a criminal underworld.

Would cannabis legalisation improve police-community relations?

A speakeasy bar during prohibition in America. Prohibition didn't stop people drinking

Jill, aged eighteen: 'I smoked cannabis every night for about a year and a half when I was fifteen and sixteen. A psychologist told me that most people he had seen who smoked it for a long time like that were affected. I was. I messed up my GCSEs because I was too busy smoking puff. My friend used to get money from her dad, she'd remove it from his pockets.

Sometimes I'd get money from my mum, I'd borrow it and sometimes we'd beg for it, just ask people by the station. It's so easy to buy drugs, everyone knows somebody. But alcohol was my real problem. I tried AA and I think total abstinence is the only model for me. If I have one that's it, I can't leave it. I saw a leaflet telling you how many units before you're off the

scale, and I realised I'd gone off the scale so I thought I'd better do something. I've been in a room full of people smoking a spliff and I've been able to say no, so eventually I think I'll be able to do that with alcohol. My drink problem isn't so bad now, but I need to sort it out before I'm forty-five and hiding bottles under my bed.'

'It is an act of grave irresponsibility to continue to force cannabis users to buy their drugs from people who are also able to supply heroin or other injectable drugs.'
Michael Gossop, National Addiction Centre, Maudsley Hospital, London, in his book *Living with Drugs* (1993)

Reaching a compromise on legalisation

'There is surely potential for compromise and a cautious step-wise approach between these extreme positions.'
Philip Robson, *Forbidden Drugs* (1994)

It is not difficult to have sympathy with the opposing points of view in the debate over the legalisation of cannabis. It makes sense for a public, official body to be appointed to explore the arguments and come up with some recommendations. To this end, Lord Mancroft recommended to the Association of Chief Police Officers in 1994 that a Royal Commission be set up to investigate the whole question:

'There is a strong case to answer, and one that bears close examination. To carry on as we are is no longer an option, and if we do not bite the bullet and make some changes, it is, I believe, inevitable that society will sustain a level of damage from which it will not easily recover. We need to examine ways by which we could bring the drug industry within the sphere of government control, as is the case with all the other industries ... we need to remove from those who are currently using drugs, and will not and cannot stop, the need first to steal from the rest of us in order to buy those drugs, and secondly the need to buy them from the black market. The black market on drugs is fuelled by money, so the first step must be to remove the profit. By supplying drugs to those who really want them through government-controlled outlets, a sort of cross between an off-licence and a chemist, at a realistic price, the need to purchase from the black market is eliminated. Clearly there would need to be restrictions as there are with the purchase of tobacco, alcohol and pharmaceuticals.'

Mancroft proposed better education on drugs and more access to help for those who need it and currently don't come forward for fear of punishment – something particularly true of young people. He noted that £35.5 billion a year is spent on drug-related crime and a mere fraction of that on healthcare services for people with drugs problems. He also insisted that any radical changes could only work in conjunction with the rest of Europe and only after public consultation and debate.

Chapter Four

Rave:

The dance drugs – ecstasy, amphetamine and LSD

Dancing the night away

This chapter is about the dance drugs, the stimulants and hallucinogens young people use to heighten their enjoyment of long nights on the dance floor: ecstasy, amphetamine, amyl nitrite, LSD.

Ecstasy is the dance drug that worries parents most, which is why I decided to devote so much of this chapter to it. Media coverage of the tragedy of Leah Bett's death after taking ecstasy on her eighteenth birthday sent shock waves through British society. Images of her grieving family are hard to forget; even harder to

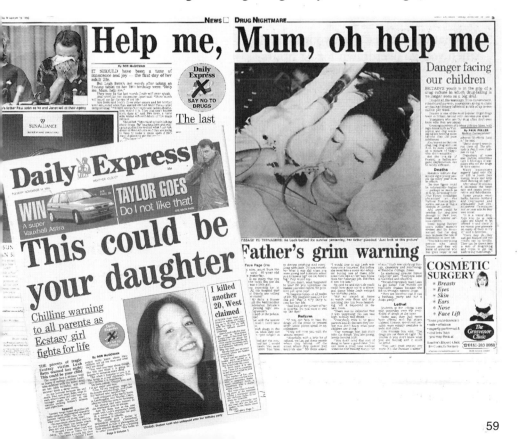

forget are the images of her in a coma, tubes in her nose. When her parents set out to campaign against ecstasy, huge hoardings of Leah's face were seen everywhere with the word 'sorted' stamped across them. That word 'sorted' is double-edged: a dealer or friend will ask a customer or fellow pill-taker if they are 'sorted', meaning have they got the pill they want? The irony of this double meaning has served to increase the impact of ecstasy on the public imagination. No wonder there is panic. Read on …

What is ecstasy?

Ecstasy comes in tablets or capsules and very occasionally as powder. The form of the tablets and capsules – their colour, shape, size and the logos embossed on them – change all the time as the manufacturers try to evade the law. The tablets, often known just as E, have an array of other names: doves, brownies, burgers, white diamonds, banana splits, love-doves, disco biscuits, New Yorkers, rhubarb and custard, shamrocks, to cite a few.

Ecstasy is a Class A drug; see Chapter seven, Drugs and the Law, for more information about what this classification means. It is defined as a 'hallucinogenic amphetamine' whose effects combine those of LSD, a hallucinogen, and amphetamine, a stimulant. But it does not usually generate the same visual distortions and illusions connected with LSD.

Ecstasy is not a new drug. In 1914 a German pharmaceutical company manufactured a similar substance to ecstasy called MDA. In the 1940s this drug was used as an appetite suppressant for curing obesity and the United States military experimented with it during the 1950s. MDA was popular with the hippies of the 1960s but banned in the United States in 1970.

Ecstasy usually comes in tablet or capsule form

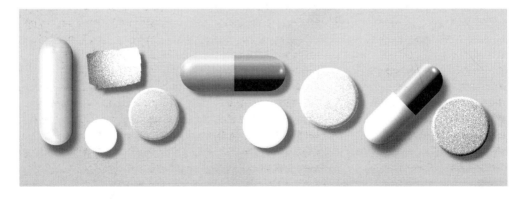

The substance now called ecstasy is scientifically known as MDMA or 3,4 **m**ethylene**d**ioxy**m**eth**a**mphetamine. MDMA remained legal until 1977 in the UK and 1985 in America; it was even possible to buy it over the counter of bars in Dallas, Texas. Like many illegal street drugs, it has a respectable, if brief, medical history: it was used to break down psychological barriers between couples during marital therapy because of its ability to elicit feelings of empathy and good will. But when more became known about its possible dangers and its public popularity mushroomed, the drug was outlawed.

One of the dangers with ecstasy is that the user doesn't necessarily know what is in it – it might be MDMA, but it will probably be cut with other substances. Over half of police seizures of ecstasy tablets and capsules have no MDMA in them. There are always rumours going round about what adulterants are in ecstasy tablets: LSD, Ketamine (an anaesthetic), methadone (a heroin substitute in tablet form) or the less harmful and more absurd dog worming tablets.

Chris, aged eighteen, says that drugs give him confidence:
'*I used to take one E and a bit of speed*, but after a while I didn't come up on one so I took more, then I took three: it takes more to get the buzz. Sometimes I take Charlie, but it's expensive. I'm not happy about it but you just have to get there again and if it takes six then fair enough. It must be dangerous to take six Es, it's a different sort of happiness you get after a while on so many, a kind of oblivion. I like doing things that are dangerous, different from normal. Perhaps it's also to do with confidence. I used to feel scared going into the classroom. You get some sort of confidence with drugs. I'm not good at being spontaneous, drugs help with that.

'Now I've been so out of it I have had no idea what's going on. I don't even know what day it is. And that's mad, I can't do that during the week. As it is, I haven't been to school on a Monday for a year, since I started raving. I do notice that my brain is definitely fucked up, I can't find words to explain things, I can't write essays. The danger doesn't stop me. I'm too relaxed about it. Nothing bothers me, nothing touches me, it's like a protection around me. I get depressed but that's because when you go back to the norm, everything is boring. I think part of my problem is the expectations on me – that I will do well, whereas I think bumbling along with half-decent grades is OK. The teachers got me a counsellor but you just want people to stay out of your way. I don't care what they say, it won't make any difference.'

Who uses ecstasy?

Estimates of numbers of young people taking ecstasy on a regular weekend basis fluctuate between 500,000 and 800,000 a weekend. The Institute for the Study of Drug Dependence (ISDD), which studied all the statistics, noted that although cannabis is easily the most popular of the illegal drugs with all users, the most significant rise in drug use in the 1990s was the upsurge in dance drugs, most popular amongst those aged sixteen to twenty-four. A survey by Release into 520 young people at dance venues in London and the South East, published in August 1997, found that almost all had tried an illegal drug at some point in their lives – two to three times as many as their non-dance clubbing peers. Eighty-seven per cent had taken an illegal drug on the evening in question, with cannabis and ecstasy being the most popular.

Parents might take comfort from knowing that the vast majority of takers, even the most enthusiastic ones, stop using ecstasy by the time they are in their early twenties. One of the most abiding drug myths is that anyone starting on 'softer' recreational drugs will end up using the 'harder' stuff later on. But the vast majority of young people taking ecstasy do not go on to other, more problematic, dangerous and habit-forming drugs. When they do, it is not ecstasy in itself that has led them on to other drugs, but a complex set of reasons to do with the individual concerned.

Donna, aged twenty: *'Drug taking on the rave and dance scene peters out at around the third year of university or college – that's around nineteen. And that's not just students, that's everybody. For students it fades out when finals loom and you can't afford to feel like shit. By twenty-one most people have stopped and only take them occasionally.'*

Not everyone needs ecstasy to enjoy themselves, but over 500,000 use it every weekend

Chris, aged eighteen, escapes from pressure:
'**The appeal of taking E or speed or Charlie**, I take them all sometimes, is that it helps you to get away, to forget the pressures of school, or parents, of things on your mind, the classic things. It seems everyone has problems at home, your parents drive you mad, they won't let you do what you want. I understand them, they don't want you going out all the time and they don't want you taking drugs. It starts with little things – being in late from school, late for meals, watching too much TV –

and then it escalates. My mother mentions drugs all the time.

'I don't binge. At some point you come down and you can't eat or sleep, you feel like shit, really drained, and you wonder why you do it, but then you remember the good times and how good it was. I didn't like it the first time. I used to go to raves and not take it. I was brought up to think drugs are only for idiots and so we used to drink on Fridays and Saturdays, we were lager louts. Then I did E because my friends did, they kept going on about how good it was.

I thought bollocks, I'll try it. I felt sort of lifted, I got into the music, the rhythm goes right through you. I depend on it to have a good time. When you take drugs you feel you have no responsibilities. At first it made me feel I was a better person and so I was not bothered by little things, and then I got laid back about more important things like school work. I'll probably do badly in my 'A' levels and I got straight As in my GCSE's. It does bother me but I'll go with the flow and pretend to myself that everything will be all right.'

How much does it cost and where do people buy it?

Ecstasy is no longer expensive and is economically attractive because the effects last through four to eight hours of raving, allowing takers to keep going without a break. But it isn't only used in the club and rave scene, says drugs worker Mike Linnell of Manchester's Lifeline:

'The price has dropped to £8 a tab so people use it to play darts on a Tuesday night. Ten years ago when we first started seeing it it was tied up with the ritual of raving. It was £25 and the price preserved the ritual, it was special. Now it's a more normal drug.'

Why is this particular drug so popular in youth culture? An explanation comes from an unlikely source, the House of Lords, where Lord Sempill said in November 1996:

'Some 2.7 million ecstasy tablets with a street value of £40.5 million, are sold in the UK every weekend. Seventeen year-olds are averaging more than £100 a month to satisfy this habit. But before we condemn them ... let us just understand what they value in this rather extraordinary pill. It kills their inhibitions and brings them into a world of love and togetherness! Is that good or bad, or is it not just what we are trying to do, albeit through different stimulants?'

The dance scene provides a huge communal sense of well being

The sinister pusher lurking at the school gates is one of the main characters in the popular drug mythology. In reality, the people selling ecstasy are likely to be those who enjoy using it themselves and are part of the rave culture. This isn't new: cannabis is, and always has been, bought and sold on the same kind of network. Buying tablets from a friend provides some small measure of protection, although the person selling them to his or her friends probably isn't going to know who made the tablets originally or what is in them because they are at several anonymous moves from the bigger suppliers.

The ecstasy experience: chasing that loved-up feeling

What attracts young people to the dance scene and its array of drugs? Ecstasy takers and ravers often use the phrase 'loved-up' when they try to explain its appeal. They feel included, part of a

Lara, aged twenty-four: *'My idea of a good night out used to be clubbing until daybreak. Now I've got a job, and my idea of a great night is to stay at home and watch TV and blob out. I've got some cocaine somewhere but I wouldn't even know where I've put it and I couldn't be bothered to take it most of the time.'*

Julie, aged forty-three: *'I once had a Nepalese Temple Ball – that's a really exotic kind of cannabis – and hid it somewhere safe in the flat I lived in at the time some twenty years ago. I wonder if they've ever found it. I hid it because I was afraid of getting busted and then just got bored with the whole business.'*

vast comforting happiness, a huge communal sense of well-being, a glittering, sparkling, emotional heaven, smiling and hugging and dancing. They do not, it seems, get tangled in the complicated sexual innuendo of the tango, rock and roll, the twist and all the variations of dance that have bedazzled generations of people for whom dancing has been a prelude to sexual liaison.

In these situations, ecstasy provides the ultimate sense of wild safety, even though safety may in reality be uncertain. It is no coincidence that two of the words young people often use to describe something they regard as good are 'wicked' and 'safe'. Kids like the idea of being wicked – but they're kids, not stunt men, and they want to be safe as well, to have fun. It's no accident that one kind of ecstasy is called Dennis the Menace and others have names reminiscent of sweets. These young people like the idea of risk, but they don't actually want to get hurt or have a bad time: 'safe' describes a good way to feel.

The August 1997 Release survey found that most of the young people said that music, socialising, atmosphere and dancing were the things they liked best about the dance scene. Drugs came fifth on the list and looking for a sexual partner was barely mentioned. However, about half did meet people with whom they subsequently had sexual relationships, even though that was not their intention in going to the dance events in the first place.

As parents, we need to take on board the idea that different drugs fit different situations and settings. The consumption of ecstasy isn't usually a private experience. It's about an instant way of overcoming alienation. It's the lively, friendly drug.

Amanda, aged seventeen, is tied down by her father: *'My problem is my father. My boyfriend got kicked out of home and so I brought him back to my house. My father went mad. He said my boyfriend was ruining the relationship between him and me. He shouldn't have done that. There had been some rows before about me raving and taking ecstasy, but that wasn't what this one was about. I don't blame him for worrying about me and about drugs, but the rows are about something else. I'm out all the time, he hasn't got a job at the moment and he's not living with my mum. Sooner or later I'll be moving out and I feel guilty so taking drugs is partly an escape from that. Sometimes I feel really bad about him because we are close and I love him, but then I think why should I be tied down because of that?'*

Ecstasy: the effects

There is a lot of hype surrounding ecstasy. Its assumed effects continue to be a favourite with newspapers, particularly the tabloids which seize on a catalogue of horrors: jaundice and hepatitis, brain swelling, brain damage, seizing up of jaws, arms and legs, severe depression, kidney failure, mental illness, heatstroke and death. It is also claimed that ecstasy causes Parkinson's Disease and senile dementia, claims for which there is as yet no hard proof.

This sort of media coverage, always going for the sensational story, adds to the fear parents feel anyway about drugs. There is no headline value in a story which says 500,000 teenagers took ecstasy and nobody was ill or died. Of course there are worrying aspects of ecstasy, but it is more helpful to take a rational rather

> **Mark, aged eighteen**: '**The first time you have E it's wicked!** The first time I had it I was fourteen and it was at a club in London. I was totally loved-up. I loved everyone and everything, everything was so cool, so beautiful, so amazing, everyone is your friend.'

RAVING MAD
Ecstasy club kids still dicing with death

LEE HARPIN and JOHN McJANNET

DAREDEVIL youngsters throughout Britain were popping deadly Ecstasy pills at the weekend — without a thought for tragic Leah Betts.

A Daily Star survey showed clubbers were still queueing up to buy the illegal £10 tablets despite days of warnings about the horrendous risks. At least 50 people in Britain are known to have been killed.

The huge demand dashes hopes that coma girl Leah did not die in vain after taking an E.

Just a few miles from Leah's home, Ecstasy tablets were openly on sale outside the Hollywood nightclub, Romford.

Teenage

Two dealers were at work in a nearby car park. Out of sight of the bouncers, they offered four different brands of E — apples, strawberries, doves and dollar pills — for £10 each.

Inside the club, four teenage boys placed tablets in each others' mouths and washed them down with water at £1.50 a bottle.

In Manchester, our reporter was approached by a youth at the Holy City Zoo and offered a whole menu of drugs — E, acid, speed ...

Drugged-up dancers moved at a frantic pace. They paused only briefly to guzzle water — oblivious to the fact that they were showing killer side-effects of Ecstasy, dehydration and over-heating.

Our investigator was hassled

twice again within the next hour by dealers selling E for between £10 and £15.

One student, called Andy, said: "It's everywhere on the club scene, especially on a gig night."

In Glasgow, one dealer set up stall beside the gents toilets at the trendy Bar 10. He was offering Doves for £15 each, stepping out-

side into the street away from the eyes of staff to complete his deals.

Doormen carried out rigorous searches of youngsters entering the Tunnel club — but many had already taken an E.

Unlucky

A teenage girl said: "It's too good a buzz to worry. The ones who have died just got unlucky."

One man, drenched with sweat, confessed: "I've had two Es and a gramme of speed." In Cardiff, the

drug made it into the Hippo Club despite the bouncers' searches. One raver, in his 20s and pouring with sweat, said: "I've had one tab of E and a bit of a whizz (Speed).

"We've all been talking about the girl who died from Ecstasy. It's sad, but it won't stop people."

Sadly, the way youngsters popped pills as if it was an every-day occurrence, was confirmed by drug charity Turning Point, who confirmed yesterday that most teenagers consider it normal behaviour.

CLUB DRUG: Ecstasy's still trendy despite tragic Leah, inset than panic-stricken and hysterical look at it. Marcus Rattray of Guy's Hospital in London, one of the few British biochemists to have received funding for ecstasy research, has said:

'... ecstasy causes big changes in the brains of animals but there is still no firm evidence that the drug is neurotoxic in humans.'

What the hype has done is to produce fear that is disproportionate to the reality. Philip Robson, psychiatrist and lecturer, writes in his book *Forbidden Drugs*:

'There are well documented records of serious physical and psychological reactions to MDMA ... many of [which] seem to have occurred in people predisposed in some way or taking large doses of other drugs as well as MDMA. It is clear that idiosyncratic reactions to modest doses do occur, though with extreme rarity, and these may prove fatal.'

There are indisputably dangers associated with the effects of ecstasy, but these are the exception and those who do get ill either already have a condition which is made worse by ecstasy or appear to have combined ecstasy with other drugs. When 'idiosyncratic' reactions occur they seem cruelly random and inexplicable but are extremely rare.

So how much truth is there to the tabloids' stories about the horrific effects of ecstasy?

Hepatitis and jaundice

There have been reports of a very few people contracting hepatitis and jaundice after taking ecstasy, but there is no hard and fast research to analyse or explain this and nobody knows exactly and categorically why these cases occur.

Swelling of the brain

Similarly, there is no final word on the very unlucky tiny minority who cannot excrete water fast enough through their kidneys after taking MDMA, a process which can lead to the swelling of the brain. What is certain is that if these tragic occurrences were common, many thousands of people would have died.

Seizing up of the jaws

Some users grind their teeth, which puts pressure on the muscles in the jaws and can leave an ache for a few hours after taking ecstasy. The incidence of jaws, legs or arms seizing up is extremely rare.

Julia, aged seventeen: *'In the hippie days it was all drugs and sex and rock and roll. These days the drugs – well, E anyway – don't necessarily make you feel like having sex. Our parents should be relieved! Their parents were all hysterical about them having sex, but E is so unsexy! You just feel more open, you feel closer to people. Speed doesn't make you feel like sex either. We take speed and E and have fun in big groups. Even when hard core was in and we wore bra tops and hot pants, it wasn't sexual, it was just about having a really good time, about having fun. I think if you drink alcohol you're far more likely to end up in bed with someone.'*

Severe depression

MDMA is linked with depression but as yet it is not known if this is temporary or may have longer-lasting effects. This issue is examined more closely later in the chapter.

Mental Illness

Another common belief is that ecstasy leads to mental illness or breakdown. There is substantial evidence that some drugs can act as triggers for mental illnesses but the strong suggestion is that this only happens when someone is already predisposed to such illnesses.

Heatstroke

Taking ecstasy can cause hyperthermia – heatstroke. Medical papers explaining the actual process of how MDMA is associated with this condition don't make for easy reading. But in his book, *E for Ecstasy*, Nicholas Saunders puts it in relatively simple, if gruelling, layman's language:

'Our body temperature has to be controlled very precisely for us to function. If we get too hot, above 42º C (108ºF), our blood starts to form tiny clots that stick to the artery walls. This is not usually a problem in itself, but the process uses up the clotting agent in the blood, so that there is nothing to prevent bleeding. There are always tiny cuts and scratches inside the body and brain which are due to the body constantly replacing worn out tissue with new cells, and normally these leaks are blocked by the clotting of blood so that you don't even notice them. But above 42ºC, bleeding is unfettered, and this is made worse by high blood pressure due to the speedy effect of MDMA and exercise. People can bleed to death in this way and if bleeding occurs in the brain it can cause a stroke.'

Because heatstroke can happen, ecstasy users in hot places like discos and parties are advised to drink a pint of water per hour and chill out regularly.

While much media attention has been paid to the incidence of heatstroke in ecstasy users, it still remains extremely rare. In a 1988 study of 143 students at Stanford University in California, a scientist discovered that forty per cent of a random sample of students had tried ecstasy at least once. Of these, ninety per cent said they felt close to other people and seventy per cent reported racing heart beat, dry mouth, tremors, palpitations and sweating. They used it sitting with friends and not in rave or club scenarios. Nobody had any serious ill effects. This study reinforces the idea that ecstasy

Paul, aged eighteen, says that parents have to listen: *'What should parents do if they find their kids are on any drugs at all, whether E or anything? You have to know your parents are there for you if you need them, they have to listen properly and not just put over their point of view. However upset they are they must listen to you. When my mum found out I'd been taking ecstasy I didn't feel judged and that was important because if I had, I'd have turned away from her. If they don't judge you then they are crediting you with being intelligent.'*

In hot places like discos, you can easily become dehydrated

deaths are linked to environment: hot, sweaty clubs and raves conducive to heat stroke. According to one study, MDMA is thought to be more potent when used in crowded conditions: experiments on mice show that MDMA is five times more toxic in crowded and hot conditions than in isolation. In the UK, ecstasy has mostly been used in hot, crowded venues.

Does ecstasy cause long-term damage?

One of the most important messages to get across to ecstasy takers is that according to the most up to date research, its *possible* long-term effects are more serious than its immediate toxic dangers. Laboratory tests on monkeys and rats show that normal doses of MDMA affected the supply of serotonin, the brain chemical which determines moods. Serotonin release by MDMA accounts for the feelings of intense empathy and friendliness common to the ecstasy experience. The bad news is that the depletion of serotonin reduces the ability of the cells in the brain to create new supplies of it. As the highly respected Parliamentary Office of Science and Technology (POST) report says:

'This damage is only slowly reversed on cessation of drug taking, and the damaged nerve cells reconnect to different parts of the brain than before, with consequences that are difficult to predict.'

The big question – does MDMA cause brain damage? – still cannot be answered conclusively. To quote POST again:

'The possibility that MDMA has damaging longer-term effects on the human brain should thus be taken seriously but remains unproven.'

Two key studies into ecstasy use have revealed further possible dangers. One was undertaken by Dr Michael Morgan of University College, Swansea in 1997. He compared three groups of people: sixteen who had taken ecstasy twenty or more times, twelve who had taken other illegal drugs but not ecstasy, and sixteen who had

---

Marjorie, aged fifty, had a fight with her daughter: *'I've read a lot about drugs* because I work in a school and all the propaganda tells you you can spot whether your children are taking drugs or not. But what can you actually do to stop them? However well read you are, however much you talk to them, how do you stop them doing it? I've talked to my daughters about everything from when they were very young, about sex, about all the dangers of adolescence. I was just unlucky, I had two risk takers. They've got into dance drugs because they're there, it's as simple as that. I have been reduced to pleading and desperation, begging them not to go out, saying, "Don't do this to us", but it's no good.

'One of them took 5 Es at a New Year's Eve party and has been depressed ever since. That was two years ago. They are children of the rave culture. You think you're safe because you live in a nice suburban area, but believe me nobody's safe. This vicious, pernicious drug thing is taking over the whole country. My kids have friends whose parents not only give them drugs, ecstasy and cannabis, but sell them to people. I have told the police, anonymously so as not to implicate my daughters. The people were cautioned but I don't think that will stop them. When one of my girls was fifteen, I looked through her things and found a tablet. I confronted her as she was going to the next rave and we had a terrible fight. I physically prevented her from going and she somehow managed to get to the phone and dial 999. She called the police because she said I was stopping her doing things she had a right to do! She was shouting at me, she said she wanted to go to raves because everyone was full of happiness and love. The police didn't come – thank God, I wouldn't have been able to face the neighbours if they had.'

never taken any illegal drug. The three groups were tested for mental agility and the ecstasy users performed significantly worse than the others. Four were so badly affected they could not even finish one test. Dr Morgan puts this down to the effect of ecstasy on levels of serotonin in the brain. In the short term, drugs like ecstasy, alcohol and Prozac raise serotonin levels. Dr Morgan predicts that the reduction of serotonin levels by damage to the receptors and neurones in the brain could cause long-term effects. He says that in the best case scenario: 'ecstasy users will react less well to stress than if they had never taken the drug'. In the worst case scenario:

'... as the users age they could lose serotonin function and be more likely to develop a mass of problems including memory deficits, depression, impulsive aggression and even be more vulnerable to Alzheimer's or Parkinson's Disease.'

Although Dr Morgan's tests do not prove beyond doubt that these are the likely outcomes, they are a warning signal to ecstasy users.

Another test on ecstasy users by Dr Val Curran at University College, London, showed that they were more depressed mid-week after taking ecstasy at weekends. Similar tests on people using alcohol found no such mid-week blues. Mike Linnell of Lifeline in Manchester reflects:

'We've seen people bang at it for six or seven years and in some cases they are very depressed, but what we don't know is if they're depressed because of serotonin depletion or whether they had such a good time, that reality has become unacceptable.'

Whatever the case, the POST report's conclusion on all the research is one that ecstasy users and their parents need to absorb:

'The studies ... strengthen concerns that ecstasy use can affect the brain some time after the immediate effects of the drug have worn off. The real fear is that ecstasy may cause long-term permanent effects on the human brain in much the same way as observed in animal experiments. This remains unproven but many experts see such long-term effects as a bigger potential threat to public health than the much more widely publicised short-term risks.'

Professor John Henry's findings add to the findings of both Michael Morgan and Val Curran. He also warns of the possible long-term effects of serotonin depletion:

'Depression is common with advancing age ... the possibility thus exists that the incidence of depression may be increased in former users of ecstasy. While there is as yet no evidence that this is the case, the possibility cannot be ignored.'

The challenge for parents, drugs workers and others in contact with young people using ecstasy, is to get it across to them that in later years they may be subject to depression as a result of ecstasy use. How effective this message will be depends on how we get through to an individual. Although kids may not like the idea of being depressed old codgers, most young people have little sense of the reality of ever getting old.

Alison, aged twenty-three, on having a good time: *'I've taken E and it's certainly not addictive*. I adored it, it was the gateway to a whole kind of music, techno and trance. People drink to lose their inhibitions and I don't like alcohol. I do like dancing and I like ecstasy for dancing, also there's no sexuality involved so you can just have a really good time and not be hassled, everyone is friendly and nobody's aggressive. I used to take it a lot a few years ago but now I can get into the music without it.'

Ecstasy and death

The media fell on ecstasy in the way they fall on Royal scandals or the lives and loves of pop stars and footballers. It combines some of the most favoured elements of an attractive story: rebellious youth, forbidden substances, night-life and death. The most telling example of this was in a tabloid newspaper's special issue on ecstasy on 17 January, 1997. Devoting its front page to a huge tablet with an E embossed on it, the headline read: 'WARNING: EVERY FAMILY MUST READ THIS – ECSTASY

A test on ecstasy users showed that they were more depressed mid-week after taking ecstasy at weekends

Picture posed by model

Lizzie, aged sixteen: '*A crucial thing for parents to realise* is that if you take E and go somewhere where there is techno or other sort of E type dance music, something with a fast syncopated beat to it, the energy generated by E helps you to key into that beat and your body and the beat become one. Before I took E the music didn't mean much to me. The fact that E related music is in all the charts shows that it's our culture in the way rock and roll and pop was for generations before.'

SHOCK ISSUE'. What followed was guaranteed to inspire dread. The editorial quoted Prime Minister John Major saying: '*Drug taking, whatever drug, tends to lead to hard drugs. Often enough tragedy occurs.*' It should be fairly clear to readers of this book by now that there is no foregone conclusion of this sort, despite its prominence as the most enduring and popular drug myth. The last two pages of the newspaper report socked home the message: 'Tragedy of 21 young victims whose lives were cruelly cut short by deadly menace of ecstasy.'

It's not that the newspaper was telling lies. It wasn't. In the years 1986 to 1997 there have been around eighty deaths in the UK with which ecstasy was linked. But the way these deaths (about eight per year) are often used in the media inspires fear without inviting a calm appraisal of the issues or analysing the actual causes of death. It also inspires a sort of guilt in the reader, who might say to him or herself: 'How can I be calm when reading of these tragic deaths? How can I appraise the facts carefully? How can I respond to my own children except to tell them ecstasy might quite likely kill them too?'

Jill, aged eighteen, can't be close to her mother: *'Everyone was doing E at the time*, it was the big thing, raves, clubs, Es. I just wanted to see what the fuss was about, it fascinated me. It seemed really exciting and dangerous as well. I took it and it wasn't what I thought it would be. I didn't like the idea that I couldn't control what I was thinking about, I felt like my brain was melting and I couldn't get my thoughts together but I liked the escape and the fact that I knew I shouldn't be doing it because it was rebellious. I had it about seven times. And then one day I took some and I had a sort of panic attack, I was depressed at the time anyway. At first it was great, but then I got claustrophobic and I thought I couldn't breathe. I was at my friend's house and I lay on her bed. E is great when it's great but when it's not everything is magnified. My friend called an ambulance and I was taken to hospital. I tried to stop them telling my mum but I was sixteen then and they said they had to. They told me that most of the cases they had as a result of E were to do with fear, and weren't really physically dangerous. My mother was really cold with me when she arrived, which was only to be expected, she was so disappointed in me. I don't blame her. I think parents just don't know how to react. She's a Christian and when we did talk about it, she said God doesn't like people to take drugs. She didn't really say much. She looked after me, that's the important thing and in a way I'm glad she kept some distance because it was easier for me.'

As it turns out, when you read this particular newspaper feature closely, you discover that of those twenty-one people who died in ecstasy-related deaths, eleven had taken ecstasy and nothing else. Others had had cocktails of drugs, or were referred to as having 'used drugs' without saying which ones. One was 'believed to have taken ecstasy', in another no traces of drugs were found but a friend said ecstasy had been taken, and another had also taken a large number of pain-killing drugs and alcoholic lemonade. How those eleven died wasn't exactly explained, apart from the case of Leah Betts.

Paul Flynn MP told the House of Commons in January 1997:

'Government figures show that, over five years, thirty-four deaths occurred in which ecstasy was the only drug involved and fifty-three occurred in which ecstasy was one of the drugs involved. The death that received a great deal of publicity on the "Today" programme was the death of a young girl a fortnight after Leah Betts died. It was described as an ecstasy death. At the inquest, it was found that the young girl had taken an unknown quantity of alcohol, one ecstasy tablet and thirty coproxamol tablets.

'The coproxamol tablets were enough to kill her three times over. Two hundred and fifty deaths a year occur as a result of coproxamol.'

If you compare the estimated number of ecstasy pills taken with the number of deaths, you see that the risk of being killed as a result of taking ecstasy is one in 6.8 million. The risk of being killed by smoking cigarettes is one in 200 or in road accidents one in 8,000. This doesn't mean we shouldn't have strong reservations about ecstasy, nor that we should say to our children: 'Go ahead and pop a pill, you've only got a one in six million chance of dying'. It means we have some grasp of the facts. Young people aren't stupid, they know it's unlikely they'll die, but tell them they will and they won't believe you. In fact, it might enhance their capacity for taking risks because they know that thousands of others like themselves have taken ecstasy, said they had a great time and been absolutely fine.

Harm reduction and minimisation

Julie, aged thirty-eight, would try to help:
'What would I do if I thought my son was taking ecstasy? God! I'd be so frightened I wouldn't want to believe it was happening. I don't think I'd punish him, I think I'd try and get some help from somewhere. It's something in society isn't it – they take it, the kids. We have to accept it and it's not going to go away. But I think ecstasy is dangerous, I only know because I've seen things on TV. Perhaps I'd ask him to tell me what it's all about and then I'd have an idea of what to do. I don't really know, I'm frightened of it all.'

The big question is how to minimise and reduce the potential harm in taking ecstasy. Leah Betts knew she needed to guard against heatstroke, a possible effect of ecstasy if certain rules are not observed. Her tragedy was that in order to keep cool, she drank not the right amount of water but too much. Professor John Henry, then a consultant at the National Poisons Unit at Guy's Hospital, said that what killed Leah Betts was probably an excess of water – some 3 litres – which made her brain cells swell and caused brain damage. For a small number of people, he explained, the drug hinders the kidneys' ability to process water and the brain becomes saturated. According to Professor Henry:

'If Leah had taken the drug alone she might well have survived. If she had drunk the amount of water alone, she would have survived.'

Imagine the scene: a club, low ceiling, bad ventilation, a great many people in constant movement and drinking alcohol to try and keep cool – the worst thing to do as alcohol actually causes dehydration. In the early days of clubbing clubs charged for water in a bid to make more money, which meant lots of young people failed to drink enough; some proprietors turned off the taps in the toilets to force their customers to buy the water for sale.

In a Commons debate in 1994, Paul Flynn MP pointed out that there had been only one ecstasy death in Holland, well known for its more liberal approach to drugs where harm reduction is the rule and not the exception. One of the problems in the UK until relatively recently has been the lack of harm reduction and minimisation, something that is now recommended by people across many of the professions involved in looking at drug use. It hit home in the government's paper *Tackling Drugs Together*, which said: 'Efforts should be made to protect those who are at risk by a range of responsible measures, often expressed as "harm minimisation".'

People who work in the UK's drugs agencies have a lot of experience dealing with dance drugs. Their methods are based on the idea of harm minimisation and reduction. They realise that telling young ravers to 'Just Say No' just doesn't work.

A similar message is coming through from the science professionals. In a medical report written in 1993, Australian scientist Nadia Solowij summed up the problems for everyone trying to understand ecstasy and get to grips with how to react to it:

'Although the incidence of extreme reaction to ecstasy is low, there is nevertheless a need to inform potential users of the risks and to minimise harm associated with its use. Consumption of large doses (acute or cumulative), history of psychiatric disturbance and pre-existing disease, appear to increase the likelihood of adverse reactions. Attempts at educational campaigns for the rave scene have involved transmission of information within the networks used by the subculture itself, e.g. flyers and magazine articles with messages to ravers to wear loose clothing, drink plenty of fluids, stop dancing when tired or when hot "chill out". Unfortunately harm reduction approaches such as this, as well as scientific reports of adverse effects, are sensationalised by the media, preventing more realistic messages getting across to the public.'

Identifying the clubs as the hotbeds of drug abuse, Barry Legg MP introduced a private member's bill into the House of Commons in March 1997, entitled 'The Public Entertainment Licences (Drugs Misuse) Bill'. Under this Bill (now an Act), a club's licence can be revoked on the advice of the local chief officer of police without any court appearance or conviction. Drugs agencies welcome aspects of the Bill but point out that it has serious drawbacks: if a club does provide chill-out areas and free supplies of water, or if there are outreach workers to assist with any drug problems or enquiries, this could be seen as evidence that there is a serious drug problem in the

Sue, aged seventeen, on drugs and being cool:
'People at Indie clubs think they're cool to take Charlie and speed and they say they don't have a good time. I don't get it. Why take speed and stuff if you don't enjoy it? I think they're arrogant when they're on coke, some say they feel like they're floating while others are throwing up in the toilets. But the idea that everyone's doing it is mad, it's only a few.'

Madeleine, aged thirty-seven, on how she thinks it starts:
'My thirteen year-old daughter Trudie doesn't play out much or hang around with the local kids but she stays for after-school clubs like dancing and goes to a youth club. I have always steered her away from the streets because I think that's where drugs are. But she does go dancing at weekends. She talked to me about the drugs, she says she doesn't want them. But then I caught her smoking and I said if you carry on you won't be able to do your dancing properly because it'll ruin your lungs. That's how it all starts, and I hope that if I keep her away from cigarettes, I'll keep her away from drugs. I don't shout at her – her dad does that.'

club and it could be closed down. Drugs are a fact of club life. Although everyone except dealers and consumers welcomes controls on drug sales in clubs, the Bill could be counter-productive, driving clubs – and dealers – underground. The more clandestine any drug activity, the more inherently dangerous for the consumer.

In Holland, pills are tested at clubs for a small fee. The Safe House Project sends teams to raves all over Holland checking the quality of the tablets being sold to ravers. While they wait, they can find out if they've been sold MDMA, what the dosage is and if it's been cut with anything else. Another service is provided whereby a tablet can be sent to a laboratory and tested; one week later a consumer will find out exactly what is in it. If it is bad, flyers are sent to clubs all over Holland warning people not to take this particular kind of tablet. This service is run by the Dance Drugs Project in Amsterdam at the Jellinek Institute, the city's main drug prevention body, and allows users to keep track of the changing tablets sold on the streets and in the clubs.

Crawford Bell of the Harm Reduction Team in Edinburgh thinks there should be similar services in the UK:

'I think we should have a system of drug testing in clubs, we should be able to take a tablet and test it. People should be able to buy testing kits and have them at home, we should promote anything that reduces harm. There were kits like this available through mail order but they were withdrawn after official pressure was put on. Under the Misuse of Drugs Act it's illegal to buy or sell drug paraphernalia.'

Drugs worker Willie MacBride of the Glasgow drugs project Enhance agrees but has reservations:

'There are problems with this kind of testing. It's a colour change test that tells whether the contents of a pill is amphetamine type drugs or opiates but it can't tell the strength of a dose or identify exactly what is in the pills. The tests aren't conclusive. The problem is that the testing could give a false sense of security. But it's a step in the right direction, it's just that everyone should be aware of the limitations.'

There are now harm reduction programmes in place all over the UK, spawned by the dance and rave culture, and drugs workers are working with club proprietors. The Bristol Drugs Project has set up its own programme, Safe and Sound, training night club owners, pub owners and staff and security (barmen, bouncers and so on) in good practice for promoters. The project's advice workers in the clubs are so popular that young people running the local dance scene mounted a benefit for them. They also have a good relationship with the local police. If a young raver is caught with drugs and cautioned, part of the deal is that they have to see one of the project's workers so that as well as the standard punishment, the young person has access to help, advice and counselling. This helps to pick up on those who have problems with drugs and may not otherwise seek help.

For five months in 1997, Glasgow's Enhance project ran a drugs awareness club in a big disused shop in the centre of Glasgow. Over eight thousand young people came in during the Friday, Saturday and Sunday opening hours of twelve to six in the afternoon. They took away 4,500 leaflets and a wealth of information. A lot of parents dropped in. Willie MacBride says that parents were for the most part expressing their fears:

'They don't know what the reality is because of all the media hype around drugs. The vast majority of young people's drug taking is

Sally, aged nineteen, on the death of her friends: *'I know two people who have died and it might be related to E. It was when I was seventeen. I didn't take any for a year because one of my best friend's ex-boyfriends had died and he had taken E so I connected it in my mind. We were in this club and we all took some pills. One guy, a real pill-head, he took loads and he really lost it on E, he was banging around, falling over, dancing like mad, he was out of control. When he got home he had a blinding headache and was convulsing, he was thrashing around. His friend got his mum and she called the doctor who sedated him and he went into a coma. The cause of death was a blood clot to the brain, I think. He was twenty-one. He had some medical history of a former blood clot, perhaps that had something to do with it.*

'Another person I know of who was twenty died of a heart attack. He had taken four pills and he'd come home feeling sweaty and having palpitations. The post mortem showed that he had MDMA and speed in his system. There are sensible ways of doing E and less sensible ways. You should always buy from people you know because some Es can be really trippy, a lot are mixed with speed and LSD. How the E takes you depends a lot on your mood. If you buy it from someone you know you're less likely to suffer from paranoia.'

Susan, aged forty, would go to the police: 'I'd punish my kids if I caught them taking anything. I know they have friends who've tried ecstasy. I'd take their money away, I wouldn't let them out. Mine are nine, twelve and fifteen. They all know about drugs from watching TV and reading teenage magazines. My fifteen year-old told me her friend had tried ecstasy but she's sensible and she never has. I tell you, if I found any of them taking anything I'd report them to the police or at the very least I'd threaten to report them. I think I would go to the police to talk to them anyway and frighten the kids and teach them a lesson. People in authority can do more than parents can. My eldest has a friend who was smoking and drinking and then took a tablet. She had to be rushed to hospital, it scared my girls. I think that's the way to stop them – scare them.'

problem free. The idea that they take dance drugs and become junkies overnight is not the reality by any means. Most don't finish up as casualties; those that do are of course worrying, but they are a small minority. Most of these kids leave drugs behind them. Perhaps it sounds trite to say it, but they grow out of drugs. They get rocked a few times but they're here to tell the tale. There's a sort of veil over the whole subject and for parents the important thing is to lift that veil so they see the reality. Drugs and clubbing are in vogue in youth culture and have been for years in a succession of youth cults.'

The London Drug Policy Forum and the Association of London Government, which represents thirty-two boroughs, has issued a code of practice under the title *Dance Till Dawn Safely*. Their bottom line is: 'While everything should be done to deter young people from taking drugs it is unrealistic to expect that this can be completely achieved.' The publication covers all the essential aspects of safe clubbing. Most metropolitan areas of the UK have similar guidelines. Ask your local drugs agency how to get copies.

So what can parents do?

From homework to ecstasy

Harm reduction and minimisation are like paramedics hurrying to the scene of an accident. They are a sort of damage limitation exercise. If we want to prevent the possibility of damage, we have to start long before there's any accident. For us as parents, damage limitation should begin when we start to communicate with our

children as babies. This is the heart of the matter. It may not be what some parents reading this book want to hear, because for them the problem is now, but it's still worth saying.

We can't be behind our kids in the queue outside the club where they might be offered a dance drug, any more than we can guide their hand during the writing of an exam paper. The trick is to get the balance between freedom and boundary right long before they are in that queue or at that party. As this mother, Nina, now in her forties, explains:

'I never worried about drugs with my daughters because it wasn't the end to start concentrating on, the end to concentrate on is giving them enough support and to get the balance right. The tricky part of being a parent is to hit the balance between freedom and support and knowing in the teenaged years how to maintain support and increase freedom. Too much freedom too early means they don't have the support and internal guidance to make wise decisions and if you're over-controlling, children might lack autonomy which would make them more vulnerable. I felt I did it really well, I don't mean there weren't conflicts and mistakes, but conflict is not negative, it's an inevitable part of balancing guidance, support and freedom.

'I don't see drugs as being different from a lot of the other aspects of the experiences of young people. I think quite non-judgementally that some young people will experiment with drugs because it's so much a part of their culture.

'What matters is that kids value themselves enough and have enough confidence and are sufficiently well informed, to take care of themselves and have sufficient self worth, and are mature enough to make sensible choices. One hopes that the process of bringing them up leaves them with a desire for their own well-being that will guide them not to make dangerous choices.'

Kim, a regular raver at the Ibiza dance club (see page 82), made sure the second time she went there on a rave holiday that she and her friends took vitamins, drank orange juice and water, ate properly, got plenty of sleep, and observed all the recommendations they'd mugged up on safe dancing. 'It's in our interests,' she says.

Nina's views are backed up by drugs worker Phil Harris of the Bristol Drugs Project:

'Drug problems are about other things for young people growing up. I'm not here talking about the harder stuff like heroin and crack – that's different. But certain other drugs are part of the lifestyle of the club scene which is very much part of youth culture, it's about young people exploring the world, and that gives rise to a lot of family tension. Just arguing about drugs and making them the main focus actually obscures the real issues. Then parents and their children can't communicate and there's a stand-off. I've seen this time and again, it's very common. Parents can't understand that their kids see drugs as a normal part of life. Parents are often angry, because it's easier to be angry when showing your concern than to be calm. Before anything can be done about drugs, people have to understand their relationships. Where there's no empathy or acceptance, there is only difficulty.'

Julian, aged eighteen, feels loved up:
'*In those days the pills really were E*, nowadays they're mostly speed I think. I took them once a week for six months, and went on for about two years. When I was sixteen it eased off, not because I was scared but because the club scene changed because hard core went out and jungle came in. At jungle raves a lot of people took crack and I found them scary. I'd never, never touch crack. Anyway I haven't got enough money to do it! People who take it say they feel so shitty the next day they just have to have more.'

The world of young people is a less certain one than that of their parents. This is an era in which young people are independent earlier. With that independence comes a desire to make your own decisions, for better or worse. Our kids are also commercialised at an early age through all the cultural influences around them. They are sucked into the market and seduced into consuming, and one spin-off from that is their desire to consume independently. Look at the offers made to them: they are bombarded with logos for things they feel they must own. From the moment they learn to recognise the brand name of a crisp packet, they are encouraged to desire brand-named clothes, games, videos, CDs, a whole teen-kiddy high street of temptation. Drugs work their way into that checklist of must-haves. This is not to condone or support consumerism, only to try to understand it. Young people can only be wise about their decisions and choices if we start early on by encouraging them not to be suckers for that consumption, but to be judicious consumers.

Cracking the code: what do our children see in ecstasy?

Parents will find it hard to have any influence over their children in relation to ecstasy (or any other drug for that matter), unless they crack the code of what kids see in them. We've all seen the horror stories about ecstasy and the kids themselves probably know someone who's had a bad time on it. So why do they go on

Kim, aged twenty, on the dream holidays of her sixteenth and seventeenth summers:
'I saved up from my after-school and weekend job and pocket money to go to Ibiza where the clubs are much more glamorous than in England – I go clubbing regularly at home of course. Lots of English kids go to Ibiza every year. So do the best DJs. I went with three other girls, it's not about meeting boys and you don't go with your boyfriend. You get the bucket shop flight at one in the morning and arrive in time to get the disco bus straight to the best club which is in the countryside, there's nothing else there. It's called Privilege and is in an enormous building with a 7,000 capacity divided into different rooms.

'You go in through a tunnel of trees and flowers, into the main room as high as an aircraft hangar with the back wall of glass so you can see right across the island. There's a swimming pool in between the two dance floors with a bridge over it and a fountain in the middle. There are tropical trees inside and comfortable benches to sit on. There's another room with cow-hide print velvet wallpaper and next to it a chill-out section with a huge bed covered in red velvet and lots of sofas. There is a restaurant and lots of bars. Below there is a croissant shop where you can get fresh orange juice and cakes. On another level there is a clothes shop and another bar. There's a balcony over the main dance floor with more bars. There's

also another vast chill-out room. Above all this is an open-air domed ceiling.

'There are thousands of young people from all over Europe and some older people too. There are spectacular transvestites in designer outfits, trapeze artists, fire eaters and people on five foot stilts diving off the stage into the pool. It's so exotic. You can't buy drugs in the club but they're easy to get in Ibiza. And you take your pill before you go in and dance all night and chill out and have an amazing time. You don't have to go to Ibiza to feel wonderful, good ecstasy makes you feel that way wherever you go, it's just that this is the best scene of all.'

Kim's first summer of holiday raving was excessive. She returned home having lost a stone doing it? It could be because they know something we don't and that we don't understand their perceptions. While we are sipping a glass of wine or downing a pint with a few friends, our kids are out dancing with hundreds of other young people.

The clubs might look like a vision of hell to the average parent of teenaged kids. The noise is at ear-bursting level, huge crowds of people are crammed in, laser and strobe lights flicker across a vast darkened dance floor where thousands of arms and legs jitter and fly. The music is of their culture, their time, and not ours. We find ourselves muttering about it in the way our parents did about the horrible sound of whatever it was we were listening to when we were teenagers. Is there anyone who wasn't told to turn down that horrible noise?

But if we want to help our children to be as safe as possible as they go out raving and clubbing, as many of them almost certainly will if they are of the age and inclination, we have to try to perceive their world from their perception. This isn't some wishy-washy trendy notion. It stems from what is in our best interests. Understanding the culture in which young people are attracted to these drugs, and why, puts the dangers more firmly in context. Getting the issues into context and perspective helps frightened and bewildered adults to feel less like strangers in this alien world and in turn makes communication with their kids more relevant, if not necessarily any easier.

Information for parents

Parents who ring drugs agencies and helplines often seem at a loss. They don't know where to start when confronted with the possibility or the fact of their children taking drugs at raves and clubs. They have found that trying to talk hasn't worked, often because they don't know what to say. Instead they shout or back off. Neither tactic is likely to make for a happy home and a well-protected son or daughter, nor does it help the parents to feel protected from their own anxieties.

Where better to start than with information? Crawford Bell of the Harm Reduction Team in Edinburgh's Community Drug Prevention Service recommends:

'Contact local drugs agencies or the National Drugs Helpline who can put you onto a local agency if you can't find one. Do that before you get to the point where you need to speak to your son

in weight, exhausted, washed-out and in need of a holiday. The next year she and her friends made a pact with each other that they would take vitamins, sleep eight hours, eat regularly and drink plenty of the right sort of fluids. They returned rested, well and the right weight. They knew what was in their own interests and for them the drugs were part of the fun, not the core of it. They knew when to stop. Of course their parents would prefer that they took no drugs at all, but if you can't stop them, you need to know they are capable of being sensible. For them the drugs were only part of the picture. Young people like Kim and her friends represent the vast majority of ravers and clubbers.

or daughter. If the parents are informed it sets an example and shows positive action to their children.'

See the section called 'Where to go for help' at the end of the book for a list of useful addresses.

Information for ravers

What we'd really like to do is successfully ban our children from taking drugs. But we realise that no matter how good our relationships with our children are, and what level of trust exists, there's a chance that they are going to try them whether we like it or not. You could tape the following list of 'do's and dont's' for clubbers and ravers to the fridge, after explaining why you are doing it. In this form, the information can be picked up almost by accident. Or perhaps you could leave it by the telephone, the loo or other places where teenagers hang out when they're at home.

This doesn't mean you are encouraging them to take drugs. It means you are showing that you have an understanding of their culture and are trying to protect them in a positive way. You could see it as the kind of sensible attitude adopted by airlines when they point out the safety procedures before a flight. Aeroplanes very rarely crash, but we still need to know the safety procedures. And knowing them reduces the chances of panic. One casualty doctor told me that most of the kids coming through her Accident and Emergency department were not ill, only in a panic themselves. They did not know how to deal with the fear of what the drug, once they had taken it, might do to them.

Safe Dancing

Don't do it. This is probably a pointless piece of advice but it's the best one. If you are determined, do it carefully.

Some drugs make you sleepy, some make you tense and panicky, some overheat you and dehydrate you. That's what ecstasy and amphetamine can do when you're dancing. Sometimes people take too much of a drug and have a bad reaction. There's no such thing as a completely risk-free drug.

Know the signs when things start to go wrong. Don't be afraid to ask for help and offer it to others who seem to be in trouble.

Never do E or any other drug on your own. Make sure others know what you have taken.

Maria, aged fourteen:
'My dad sort of knows about me taking trips and speed and Es. He thinks that's what young people do. I know he tried drugs when he was young and he's not hypocritical. I've only ever taken drugs for fun, no other reason whatsoever. If I was in trouble I'd definitely talk to my mum and dad about it. Once my friend I was with had gone home with a strange man, we'd been taking speed, and it was scary because we were only fifteen and I felt responsible for her. I told my mum and somebody went to fetch my friend. Mum brought me vitamins and orange juice and made sure I was OK. She didn't tell me off at all. She just wanted to make sure I was all right. I was really appreciative that I could tell her I'd taken speed and been scared about my friend. Of all my friends, I'm the only one that can tell her parents. Most of them, if their parents found out they'd go mad. Most parents would rather not know I think, even if it's happening right in their faces.'

Know your dealer. With ecstasy you never know what you're taking, but experience proves that knowing who sells you a tablet helps to safeguard you. Never take ecstasy from strangers.

Take half a tablet and see if it affects you badly. If it does, don't take the rest. Don't take more than one tablet per rave: restrict your consumption to one or two a month. Many ravers stick to this. The few who don't need to rethink their habits.

Try not to panic. But if you start to feel panicky, which can happen with ecstasy, LSD, magic mushrooms and a lot of cannabis, tell someone who can help you to calm down.

If you are OK but someone else is panicking, calm them down and reassure them. Stay away from noise and flashing lights. Talk them down reassuringly and soothingly. Don't panic yourself if they don't seem to respond. Get help. Don't worry about annoying your friends or getting into trouble because you or your friends have taken drugs, it's infinitely more important to make sure people are looked after.

If someone is breathing unnaturally, get help.

Overheating and dehydration

You can get overheated with dance drugs like ecstasy and amphetamine which allow you to dance for prolonged periods. If you are very high you may forget to drink regularly. Have regular intakes of water, fruit juices and soft drinks – about a pint an hour, not more. Don't drink alcohol, it dehydrates the body further.

Overheating and dehydration can be very serious. The signs are:

- Cramps in legs, arms and back

- Failure to sweat

- Sudden exhaustion

- Feeling the need to urinate but producing very little

- Fainting.

What to do

You can avoid all this potential trouble by:

■ Not taking drugs

■ Not dancing for long stretches of time

■ Having regular chill-out and rest

■ Wearing loose clothes

■ Not wearing hats, which keep heat in the body

■ Remembering that ecstasy is never as good again as the first few times you take it. Don't try to achieve that first high by increasing the dose. It only makes the whole exercise more dangerous.

Be cool

If you or a friend are dehydrating:

■ Don't wait until the crisis is out of hand. Get help, either from an outreach worker or paramedic if there's one there, or by dialling 999 for an ambulance

■ Go somewhere really cool – outside if necessary

■ Splash with cold water

■ Some people are only alive because sensible friends knew first aid. Get some basic training from your local St John's Ambulance service. If you're at school, suggest it's taught there

■ Get a copy of one of the safer dancing guides from your local drugs agency. Ring the National Drugs Helpline or look through the addresses at the end of this book. Keep it in the house, read it, absorb its information, chat to your friends about it

■ Although amphetamine is not directly implicated in dance scene deaths in the same way as ecstasy, it can have the same overheating and dehydration effects. So you need to observe the same recommendations.

The other dance drugs

The other drugs that fall into the dance drug category are amphetamine, commonly known as speed, LSD and amyl nitrite. More young people experiment with these than with ecstasy,

19 year-old Sally describes a bad time on ecstasy and what she did: '*I had a bad time on E once*. *I took it and went onto the dance floor. I went to the ladies twenty minutes after taking it and saw how ashen-faced I was, and my jaw was wobbling from side to side. Sometimes E makes you grind your teeth and chew the inside of your mouth. I've had that loads of times, you get spasms in your jaw. But this time I was really freaked out and I knew it wasn't a nice pill. I felt really paranoid, I knew I was going to feel horrible for however long it lasted – between two and six hours roughly. I wasn't in control of my body.*

'I sat down and my friends asked me if I was OK, I said I was, I didn't want to admit it because that would have made it more real and I didn't want it to be. I thought how awful, I'm eighteen and I'm going to die of E. I felt as though the pill I had been given was really a tranquilliser because everything went blurry and I lost all feeling in my legs. I couldn't stand up. A friend came over and I asked for water and then she and the others got me outside. I was retching. My eyes started rolling, I was petrified.

'My friends took me to a twenty-four hour medical station especially for raves. I think it wasn't E that I took but ketamine or something. Eventually, we got to someone's flat, they gave me water, toast and tea and although I went on shaking and going hot and cold, after a while I began to feel better. It was another year before I took any more E, but when I did I made sure I knew the person who gave it to me and only took half. I felt nicely stoned. It was in the day time at an outdoor cafe, there was food and drink and lots of people, it was a really nice atmosphere. Another day I took a quarter and it was fine. I've done it four times since then and it's been fine.'

although ecstasy is the one that has caught the attention of parents. The Institute for the Study of Drug Dependency (ISDD) estimates that 'about one in seven young people (fourteen per cent) will have used amphetamine or LSD, one in ten amyl nitrite, and about one in twelve (eight per cent) will have tried ecstasy'. One in ten are also thought to have tried magic mushrooms, which are not strictly speaking dance drugs and fall into the category of recreational drugs; like LSD, they are hallucinogens.

These statistics sound alarming. But when you unravel them you find that they refer to how many young people *ever tried* these drugs. It could mean they have only had them once and does not indicate habitual use.

Amphetamine

What is it?

Amphetamine is a stimulant and its use dates back to the 1880s. The name is an acronym for **a**lpha-**m**ethyl-**phe**ne-**t**hyl-**amine**. A synthetic drug, it was discovered in Germany and used as a stimulant and a tonic. It has had many medical uses and was sold over the counter in the United States as a nasal decongestant until 1971. During World War Two, 72 million amphetamine tablets were issued to British troops to keep them awake and alert and in the early 1960s millions of prescriptions were issued for amphetamine in Britain. Benzedrine, an amphetamine-based drug, was thought to help in curing thirty-six ailments including migraines, seasickness, obesity and impotence. It was used commonly until it came under the Misuse of Drugs Act in 1964; even Prime Minister Anthony Eden during the Suez crisis said he was 'living on benzedrine'. But when some of its adverse effects started showing up, attitudes to the range of drugs known as amphetamines changed. That doesn't mean amphetamine has gone out of style: despite its current illegality, its popularity persists. It is usually known as speed, whizz or bang.

How is amphetamine used?

Nowadays its most common recreational form is as amphetamine sulphate, sold as a white crystalline powder which most users sniff up their noses. Others report that they rub it against their gums, which gives an indication of its strength by how much tingling it causes. Inhaling it up the nose is not necessarily a pleasant experience, as one user says: 'It feels sharp and acrid in the nose when snorted, and it doesn't give the easy exhilaration of cocaine. It just makes my heart pound as everything becomes fast and urgent.' Some people swallow it dissolved in a drink or wrapped in a cigarette paper. A very small number of users inject it, a dangerous practice which is discussed in detail in Chapter five, Beyond the Rave.

Amphetamine costs about £5 to £10 for a 'wrap' – so called because it is sold in small folded bits of paper. This can make it tempting as the least expensive, main illegal street drug. As with ecstasy, users can never be sure what they're buying and it is often cut with other things such as soda, caffeine, milk powder, glucose, Vitamin C, chalk, talcum powder and very occasionally dangerous poisons.

Natasha, aged seventeen, says popping a pill is cheaper than drink: *'Most people I know take drugs. Everyone smokes weed and practically everyone I know takes Es, speed and Charlie – cocaine. They don't take it all the time but they do on a night out. Maybe twice a month or something on average. That's about how much I take drugs now, although I used to take a lot more. If I do take E, I almost always share one tablet with someone else. I'm a student so in term-time I take them about once a month but in the holidays I take more. If I think it's at all scary, I don't take it but I almost always have just one, it's so small, you think how could it possibly hurt you? We often get drunk at college but it's much easier and cheaper to pop a pill. I only buy them from people I know and my friends do the same.'*

A 'wrap' of amphetamine

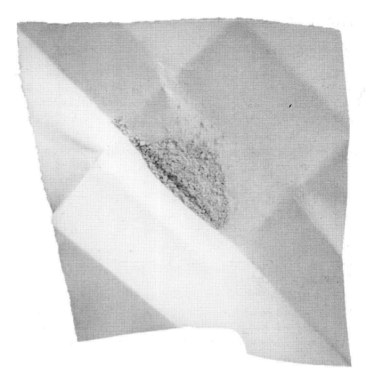

Other kinds of amphetamine include dexamphetamine, known as dexies; methylphenidate, known as Rit; methylamphetamine, known as meths or crystal; Durophet, known as black bombers; and methamphetamine, known as Ice. Few if any of these variants are currently popular on the British dance scene, although there is some evidence of Ice being used. Ice is about twice as potent as amphetamine in its more usual form but is rarely seen in this country. There is also a form of amphetamine known as base, which is to amphetamine what crack is to cocaine. It is much stronger and more compulsive. This drug is not yet widely used in the dance scene, but some drugs agency workers have reported hearing about it in London and the South West of the UK.

The experience of amphetamine

The attraction of amphetamine is that it increases the metabolic rate and gives the user added energy. Like ecstasy, it can keep people going for hours, which is why it is so popular as a dance drug. It suppresses the need for sleep or food and can create a sense of euphoria. Breathing and heart rates increase and blood pressure rises.

People who use amphetamine talk about getting a rapid high and being imbued with a sense of capability and confidence. They say it enhances concentration and increases their powers of perception. They tend not to get hungry or tired. It's not easy to identify which drug someone might be using by looking at them or observing their behaviour unless they are very high or stoned. But the old image of the 'speed-freak' is of someone who is speedily immersed in whatever they are doing, bright-eyed and extra alert, barely pausing as one might normally. They might be dancing, talking, or going for a very long walk. As the effects wear off, most recreational users will feel tired and perhaps anxious and depressed, but as long as they sleep and eat properly they should not experience any long-term problems.

Dangers associated with amphetamine

Like ecstasy, amphetamine is not a drug on which people can become physically dependent. But as with anything associated with pleasure or vitality which alters mood (alcohol, gambling, chocolate, sex), compulsion and craving can develop. In the short term, once the energy rush has worn off, the user might come down heavily from the drug and feel lethargic and depressed. The longer use continues, the worse the 'crash' (the come-down) will be, but usually there are no long term or serious effects and a few days' rest and proper food will put someone back on line.

If it is used a lot, amphetamine can make people more vulnerable to colds and infections. This is not because of the drug itself, but because of the lifestyle that sometimes accompanies it: users don't eat properly and so debilitate themselves. Repeated and prolonged use of amphetamine can provoke emotional disturbance, but in itself in smaller, less habitual recreational style doses, the drug doesn't cause these problems. There is some evidence that long-term repeated use can cause nerve damage, high blood pressure and irregular heart beat, but this is rare.

A survey carried out in 1979, after some forty years of widespread use, found that there had only been seventy-nine deaths associated with amphetamine. Many of these were the result of the rare and dangerous practice of injecting it. Since 1985 there have been some ninety-seven deaths associated with amphetamine. The cause of death remains predominantly associated with injected use of the drug, leading to overdosing or other complications connected to that method of transmission. In contrast to the closely related drug MDMA, the POST report says there is 'no evidence linking moderate doses of amphetamines to deaths through hyperthermia'.

Amphetamine base

Amphetamine base is a lumpy white crystal or paste which is dabbed on to the gums or tongue but not smoked. It is much stronger than sulphate, the kind of amphetamine most popularly used. Little is known about the prevalence of this type of the drug in the British recreational drug scene. Although it is around, drugs workers at agencies all over the UK say it is thought to be pretty rare. But it's as well to be warned about it. Sally Murray of Kaleidoscope says:

'We are seeing a big upsurge in amphetamine use, but not so much on the counselling side. It's more that we're hearing from young people and street drugs workers that it has become the drug that replaces ecstasy when ecstasy gets boring or they've had a bad experience with it. What is more worrying is that we are hearing that people are using amphetamine base which is a much stronger form of the drug.'

Amphetamine psychosis

Amphetamine psychosis is brought on by extensive and obsessional use of the drug. As with other drugs, for those for whom it becomes a problem, there is usually an underlying psychological reason for over-use. When someone experiences amphetamine psychosis, they become delusional and paranoid, seeing things and people that aren't there and experiencing hallucinations. Unlike psychosis caused by mental illness, the psychosis disappears once the drug is no longer used; this usually takes a few days, although full recovery can take longer. Although psychosis is usually associated with a few who have used the drug long term and obsessively, amphetamine use could trigger psychosis in someone who is already predisposed to it. Sally Murray says:

'My concern is that although such psychosis is rare, it's serious, and that amphetamine base, being so much stronger, will do far more damage if it gets a hold, than amphetamine sulphate.'

LSD, magic mushrooms and amyl nitrite

What is LSD?

The full name of LSD is lysergic acid diethylamide. It is a hallucinogenic drug, which means it induces hallucinations and alters perceptions. In its basic and original form, it is related to a fungus called ergot which grows on rye and was used for centuries as an aid to childbirth. In the middle ages, people would sometimes accidentally eat ergot and have convulsions and hallucinations. LSD as we know it was discovered in 1943 by Dr Albert Hoffman, a Swiss scientist who was working on ergot derivatives. By mistake he ingested some and experienced fantastic visions:

'I lost all account of time. I noticed with dismay that my environment was undergoing progressive changes. My field of vision wavered, and was distorted like the image in a curved mirror ... like the reflection in an agitated sheet of water ... with my eyes closed, colourful and changing fantastic images invaded my mind continuously. It was especially remarkable how all sounds ... were transposed into visual sensations, so that with each tone and noise a corresponding coloured image, changing in form and colour like a kaleidoscope was produced. I was overcome with fear that I was going out of my mind. Occasionally I felt as if I were out of my body. I thought I had died. My ego seemed suspended somewhere in space ... I woke up the next morning somewhat tired but otherwise perfectly well.'

LSD became infamous in the 1960s when it was eulogised by the counter-culture guru, Timothy Leary

Cary Grant said he felt 'born again' after taking LSD

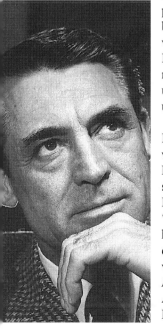

LSD was used in psychiatry for many years and was explored by the United States secret services as an aid to interrogation and brainwashing. It was also used medicinally for terminally ill patients, but all these uses died out and recreational use of the drug became popular. LSD became infamous in the 1960s when it was eulogised by counter-culture guru Timothy Leary and the American hippies, who said that it gave them the opportunity to expand their minds. Hallucinogens have a centuries-old history of ceremonial and religious use, and some of the claims made for LSD by people using it these days are similar to ones made by these ancient users.

Its contemporary popularity is not confined to hippies and whacko Harvard academics like Leary. Time-Life president Henry Luce said it gave him a glimpse of God, and Hollywood star Cary Grant said that he felt 'born again' after taking it. Leary, who described his experience of hallucinogens as being 'swept ... into a maelstrom of transcendental visions and hallucinations', advised the world to 'Turn on, tune in and drop out'. LSD was popular with a whole batch of high profile writers in the 1950s and 60s like Aldous Huxley (*The Doors of Perception*), Ken Kesey (*One Flew Over The Cuckoo's Nest*), Allen Ginsberg, the well known beat poet, and William Burroughs, best selling novelist (*The Naked Lunch*).

Much of the LSD sold in the 1990s is less powerful than the mind-blowing stuff of the Leary era, down from an average of 250 micrograms to around 50 micrograms, and it has become part of the dance scene. It is a Class A drug.

What does it look like?

LSD, known as acid, is usually sold on little bits of thick paper impregnated with LSD, which dissolve on the tongue. They are often embossed with an image or logo. They sometimes have pictures of cartoon characters on them like Bart Simpson, Batman, Sonic the Hedgehog or the Pink Panther, and have names like Strawberries or Chinese Dragon. LSD is also sold as tablets, capsules or on little bits of gelatin, and occasionally on sugar cubes. These are known as tabs and cost about £4 each.

The experience of LSD

LSD can provide the most powerful sensations of any of the street drugs. Taking it is described as 'tripping'. As one experienced user says:

LSD is usually sold on little squares of impregnated paper with printed images on them

Tanya, aged sixteen, had a bad LSD trip: *'I was really shy and didn't talk to people* or socialise so I started puffing when I was about thirteen or fourteen. It was wicked, I could chat to anyone, it gave me confidence. Then I tried E when I was fifteen because everyone else did it. I loved it, it was brilliant. Then I did it every weekend for three months, I'd have no sleep for forty-eight hours and then I had a really bad experience. The circumstances weren't right and I took one pill and then another half and I started shaking, my teeth were grinding. And then last summer I tried LSD and completely freaked out. I haven't been living at home because I didn't get on with my stepmother and my father said, in the nicest way possible, that I would ruin their relationship if I stayed with them so I had to leave.

'The LSD was terrifying. I was laughing and crying, it was really weird. After I took it I went on having flashbacks which fucked me up and I haven't taken any drugs since then.

I went to the GP who told me to tell my parents, so that's when I told my dad. I was living at home at the time. He didn't talk to me, he left leaflets in my room. But now I think he loves me less. He looks at me in a different way. The flashbacks went on for months. I found a counsellor who talked to me about the problems with my family and other things, and gradually the flashbacks wore off. They were so frightening, sometimes they'd last for six or eight hours. The thought of drugs or alcohol really scares me now.'

'It's not addictive because it's too exhausting and not just pleasure-giving. But it fills you with exciting, truly positive feelings about yourself and the world. On acid you can make great sense of everything in ways that stand up to the test of sobriety, although you also have to be prepared for rare moments of the opposite: frightening mental confusion. You have to be unafraid of letting your mind roam; people who try to control their thoughts too much can become very anxious, and those who are really frightened of having a bad trip can find their fears self-fulfilling.'

People sometimes take small amounts of LSD to go dancing. Then, as one user explains:

'Lights and objects shimmer and glow as they always do on acid, but the effect on the mind is more controllable.'

LSD is unpredictable. It is impossible to know how much acid has been blotted onto the tab or how recently it was done, or what it might be cut with.

A good trip can be like a highly exotic series of revelations, extraordinary visions, amazing thoughts, out-of-this-world sounds and marvellous sensations. A bad trip can feel like being in your own worst nightmare. Users can experience both the good and the bad in the same trip.

The effects of LSD

LSD's hallucinogenic powers can create illusions and delusions. A few people have died as a result of imagining they could accomplish the impossible while under the influence of the drug, but these deaths were mostly a long time ago, mostly in the United States and very few and far between. The idea of the LSD death far outstrips the reality. Most people know their illusions are not real and that they are imagining things rather than actually seeing them. For example, one user reports opening a fridge and seeing ice creams move, which she found hilarious and a little alarming, but she knew they weren't really moving.

LSD has been held responsible for damage to chromosomes. But Michael Gossop of the National Addiction Centre at the Maudsley Hospital writes:

'... the few reports that suggest the drug does cause damage of this sort have exposed cells to massive concentrations of LSD and for unrealistically long periods of time. Even so, they have failed to prove that the resulting damage is any greater than that produced by many commonly used substances. One study found that aspirin and LSD led to comparable levels of chromosomal breakage.'

LSD can also cause flashbacks; occasionally, sudden visual hallucinations have been reported by people weeks and in some cases, years after they had taken the drug. However, no evidence has ever been provided to prove that it causes permanent harm.

What to do if someone needs help

If you know that your son or daughter, or anyone else, is 'tripping' it is essential to be calm with them and to reassure them if they are anxious. By responding to their needs – perhaps to be held or listened to or taken for a walk – you will help them come through it more easily. Because LSD is so powerful and unpredictable, people with an unclear sense of themselves might feel confused, anxious and frightened. There is no permanent damage associated with LSD, so if someone is scared, they need gentle talking down and encouragement not to worry. It is not a drug like solvents or ecstasy, where in extreme cases people are very occasionally in life-threatening situations. The only threat from LSD is that if a trip goes wrong, someone could be in danger of having an accident. This too is rare.

The same things apply to LSD as to many of the other drugs: parents will be horrified at the thought of their children taking LSD, but if they can't stop them they can advise them of the safest way to do it. It's never a good idea to take drugs alone, and among the recreational drugs, this is perhaps especially true of LSD. Because LSD can create such powerful sensations, it's always best to take it with someone who is 'straight', not under the influence of any drug themselves. If the person who is tripping needs some kind of reassurance, their friend will be able to give it.

As parents we need to know that whatever wild things people on an LSD trip may do or say, in safe circumstances they can come to no harm, and in the vast majority of cases will not be permanently affected in an adverse way. Whatever we might think about LSD, we have to understand that for many young people, it represents the most exciting and weird ride in the whole psychedelic funfair of drug psychodrama.

Magic mushrooms

Magic mushrooms is the name for those fungi which are hallucinogenic. There are hundreds of varieties; in the UK, there are ten which have the chemical constituent which causes people to get high on them. They are estimated to have been tried by about seven per cent of teenagers.

The history of magic mushrooms dates back hundreds of years and they are still used in some Central and South American cultures as a means of reaching into the inner recesses of one's own spirit and the outer reaches of the spirit world. The contemporary use of magic mushrooms in the UK is thought to have arisen as people looked for alternatives to LSD; they are not illegal unless 'prepared' – cooked or crushed – and they are organic, so are perhaps seen to be less threatening. You eat what you pick, so as long as you pick the right mushroom you know what you are putting in your mouth.

There are two groups of magic mushrooms which people consume in the UK. One group contains the chemicals psilocybin and the much more potent psilocin. The other group contains ibotenic acid as its psychoactive ingredient. The most popular magic mushroom in the UK is *Psilocybe semilanceata*, known as the Liberty Cap. Users generally take between one and thirty; the more that are taken, the stronger the trip. The other popular mushroom is *Amanita muscaria*, commonly known as Fly Agaric. This is much more potent, so users usually take fewer.

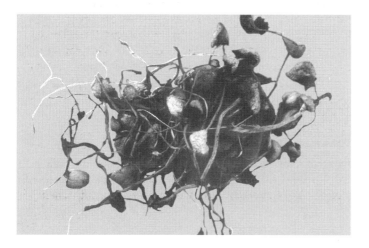

The most popular magic mushroom in the UK is the Liberty Cap, which contains the psychoactive chemical, psilocybin

The experience of mushrooms

The strength of the hallucinogenic experience of magic mushrooms depends on mood, setting, personality and so on. It is not unlike that of LSD but tends to be milder and not to last as long, although there is no hard and fast information on this, and how long a mushroom eating experience lasts can vary. If they take a relatively low dose – a few mushrooms – users can feel pleasantly euphoric as they might with smoking cannabis, but if they take more of them, the experience escalates and then it can be like an LSD trip.

Are mushrooms dangerous?

There are very few magic mushroom casualties as far as is known, and no deaths are recorded. The greatest danger is from picking and eating a poisonous variety of mushroom. Because the experience is not unlike that of LSD, it's possible that if the taker is in a frame of mind that is not conducive to enjoyment, he or she might feel anxious and paranoid as a result. There are no significant withdrawal symptoms, and no long-term physical or mental consequences.

What can parents do?

There is no really serious danger with magic mushrooms, but if parents know their children are going to try them and can't stop them, then they would be well advised to get them a good book showing them which are the mushrooms they actually want. An example is the Collins *Guide to Mushrooms and Toadstools*. Several varieties of mushroom growing wild in the UK are lethal, so anyone thinking of using magic mushrooms needs to be sure they are not going to eat something poisonous. They also need to know that if they feel sick, they should get help and go to a hospital casualty unit, taking a sample of the mushroom with them.

We need to get through to our kids that while they might get into trouble for taking drugs, if they look for help, the consequences won't be half as bad as they might be if they don't. Better still, we need to find ways of curbing our fear and fury so that if they need us they feel they can come to us without hesitation or trepidation.

Poppers are sold in small bottles. Sniffing produces a short-lived dizzying rush of blood to the brain

Amyl nitrite

Amyl nitrite is not an illegal drug. It is sold in little bottles from which the liquid can be sniffed. Known as 'poppers', the bottles have names like Ram, Stud, Locker Room, Liquid Gold and many others. They are sold in sex shops and have crept into the dance scene. The only illegal aspect of poppers is under the Intoxicating Substance Supply Act, selling them to people under eighteen for the purposes of getting high.

The effects of sniffing are to feel a minute-long but massive rush of blood to the brain. It is a dizzying, throbbing sensation that is sold as an opportunity to enhance orgasm. It would seem to give no more than a thrill, and it is a drug users soon tire of. There is no danger of dependence. The danger of poppers arises if people drink them, get them in their eyes or on their skin. Drinking them is very dangerous and anyone who does that needs to get to hospital. Splashing in the eyes requires water to wash it out and skin problems arise when people soak a hanky in it and then hold it repeatedly to their faces. The ISDD says that one in ten young people admit to having tried poppers; 'tried' does not mean habitually used.

Nina, aged forty-seven, on loosening the reins:
'What matters is that **kids value themselves** enough and have enough confidence and are sufficiently well informed to take care of themselves and have sufficient self-worth and are mature enough to make sensible choices and pick their way through. Their well-being will guide them not to make dangerous choices.

'The absolute key is to find a pace that works for both parents and their children in loosening the reins while maintaining support. I felt I did it really well, I don't mean there weren't conflicts and mistakes, but conflict is an inevitable part of guidance, support and freedom. Of course there were rules, they weren't allowed out during week nights when they were at school and on Fridays and Saturdays they had to be in by ten one night and midnight the other when they were fourteen or fifteen.

'You aim to give children a sense of the long term because as they grow up they have to develop that. As time goes on you swap responsibility from you to them, giving them their freedom but letting them know you're there for them if they need support. Conflict is a sign that you've reached a point where there's a need for re-negotiation so what often happens is a set of rules about times of coming in, or doing home work and all that. It works for a while but when it ceases to work it's time to re-negotiate. I felt we talked enough about drugs. I never felt that saying don't do something is a very good strategy, it is better that the judgement comes internally from themselves, whether it's about sex, contraception, fast driving, working for exams, drugs – it applies to everything.'

Finding a Clearer Path

Imagine in about ten or fifteen years time, when today's ravers are parents of young children. They won't be popping pills and dancing until dawn any more than most parents of any generation. It's a comforting thought. Remember the reckless moments of your teenaged years. Look back and try to imagine what your ideal parents would have said and done. Nobody can match the ideal, but we can try to defuse the panic, find a clearer path through the drugs minefield and see the facts for what they are. We can try to sort out what the best approach is to our children, to instil confidence in them, introduce them to freedom without letting them go too soon, and let them go without holding them back when they need to explore their independence. We can be one step ahead by knowing what drugs are really about. When they are little, we kneel down to communicate with them. When they are big, we have to know how to look them in the eye and how to find a way of appreciating how they see the world.

Chapter Five

Beyond the rave:

Heroin, cocaine and crack

The sniffers, puffers, dancers and ravers, eaters of mushrooms and experimenters are extremely unlikely to go beyond the rave and on to heroin, cocaine or crack. It helps to remind ourselves that the young people who are trying drugs are for the most part doing just that – trying them a couple of times, using them for a while recreationally, not getting into problems with them, and leaving them behind. Of all those who have tried drugs, less than one per cent have tried heroin, crack or cocaine. Of these, fewer than 0.5 per cent have injected the drugs.

But this isn't any comfort to parents whose sons and daughters are using heroin, cocaine or crack. Later in this chapter we look at what can be done to help those parents and their children.

Heroin

People who become dependent on heroin and other heavy-end drugs have almost always suffered an emotional drama early in their lives which has never been resolved. To put this picture into perspective, let me tell you the story of Johnny, who is twenty-eight. He uses heroin and has done so every day for many years. He started using drugs when he was thirteen but his route to drugs began a lot earlier, long before he'd even heard of them or come into contact with anyone using them – even the experimenters. I met him and a friend of his called Andy, also dependent on heroin, at Kaleidoscope, the drug dependence unit in Kingston-upon-Thames. Both were drowsy when they spoke to me, their eyes almost closing, their sentences trailing off.

Johnny's story

Johnny told me he had perfect parents, a lovely home, a fine upbringing. He had no problems with his family at all. Johnny's parents were reasonably strict, but nothing unusual. They loved him. But he was a rebel, he just liked taking risks, he liked that kind of life. Danger and trouble attracted him. That was just the way he was. He said: 'I was the youngest and I was pampered, that's why I was a rebel.' Then he went on to say that his two older brothers had regularly set about him – not badly, he said, just enough for a few bruises: 'just the normal stuff'. It started from as early as he could remember and went on until he got big enough to defend himself. Everyone thought it was normal.

As he got older he became increasingly rebellious. His parents would shout at him. But then they realised there was no point in shouting at him. 'My mother would say, "Where did I go wrong?".' Johnny found that unbearable. He was eleven when she first said it and it hurt him terribly that he couldn't explain to her that she had done nothing wrong. He became more rebellious still, and then drugs became a means of taking risks and rebelling, and a source of temporary comfort. He started with glue sniffing. Then he tried cannabis and from there, in search of ever deeper oblivion, he tried heroin. It's not that one drug was a gateway to the next, more that to escape the pain he had never acknowledged, he blundered on to ever stronger forms of chemical oblivion.

It had never occurred to Johnny that he had as much of an unaddressed trauma in his life as Andy, whose story was so clear: Andy had seen his father die under a collapsed wall and felt responsible, his mother had beaten and rejected him and threw him out when he was thirteen. Johnny said nothing bad had ever happened to him, there were no mitigating factors, he was just a rotten apple. But from Johnny's own unwitting account, we have a classically bullied small child. Johnny's parents were not on the face of it to be blamed for Johnny's rebelliousness. But what kind of society accepts such bullying as normal? While one child in a family might emerge relatively unscathed from regular beatings, tauntings and bereavement, another can't. And the traumas of childhood don't have to be apparently major ones like bereavement. A 'normally' bullied boy like Johnny can internalise that experience and suffer the consequences. No two children's experiences are the same.

What is heroin?

Heroin is an opiate derived from the poppy, *Papaver somniferum*. Its street names are smack, brown, gear, junk or skag and it is a Class A drug. Its basic product, opium, has been around for as

Poppy cultivation in Manchuria in 1907

long as history has recorded medicinal and ceremonial uses for drugs derived from plants. There are other opium derivatives commonly used by doctors that will be familiar to some readers, such as codeine, diconal, pethidine and omnipon. In its illegal form, people either snort powdered forms of the drug, smoke them or dissolve the powder in water and inject it. Pure heroin is white powder, but the usual street heroin is brownish.

An opium den in the East End of London in 1870

The raw materials for making the drug come from Turkey, Iran, Iraq, Afghanistan, India, Nepal, Bangladesh, Burma, Thailand, Laos, Mexico, Colombia and other South American countries. Some of these are places where drugs underpin whole economies; drug cartels have turned to growing opium poppies as well as coca from which cocaine and its derivatives are made. Heroin is more easily available and cheaper than in the past, and is now sold in a smokable form known as 'brown'.

A brief history of heroin

As far back as ancient Greek mythology, the goddess Demeter discovered that opium soothed her sorrows. Opium, from which heroin was eventually derived, has always been admired for its sedative powers. It found its way to Europe and hit England in the sixteenth century when it was mixed with spices and alcohol and became a much used and highly effective drug called 'laudanum', which is a Latin word meaning 'worthy of praise'. English literature is full of writers who used laudanum: Thomas de Quincey, Samuel Taylor Coleridge, Wilkie Collins, Charles Dickens and Elizabeth Barrett Browning, among others. It was common to put a bit of opium in a pint of beer, and poppy head tea was available from chemists until the 1950s. Morphine, the drug that paved the way for the manufacture of heroin, was discovered in Germany in 1805 and named after the Greek god Morpheus, god of dreams. In 1874, a form of that drug called diacetyl morphine was made and was named *heroisch,* meaning 'powerful' in German. It was used as a remedy for morphine addiction and is the beginning of what we now call heroin.

As opium use grew in the West at the start of the twentieth century, world conferences were organised at which some thirty countries agreed to restrict medicinal and other uses of opium and its derivatives. In the United States in 1914, the route taken was to indict users through the criminal justice system. In the UK in 1926, the Rolleston Committee advised that dependence should be seen as an illness requiring medical treatment rather than a crime requiring punishment, and the British system for the treatment of opiate users began: it was thought better as a last resort to maintain those who were dependent on prescribed doses of drugs, rather than penalise them. The system still exists, although the numbers of people legally receiving heroin are small compared to estimates of users buying the drug through the illegal street trade. In his book *Forbidden Drugs,* consultant psychiatrist Philip Robson points out that this British response and approach might have had something to do with the fact that at the time, the drugs picture was very different: heavy-end use was more common amongst the professional and middle classes, people with the clout to influence decision makers.

Charles Dickens was one of the many literary figures who used laudanum, a mixture of opium, spices and alcohol

In 1925 heroin was outlawed in the United States. Suddenly 500,000 dependent users were without their supply and the black market, identifying a fantastically lucrative business, manufactured heroin in secret laboratories. The illegal trade is now entrenched all over the world. It seems that more heroin is getting into the UK in the 1990s, but increased seizures by police and customs could also indicate their growing efficiency. What is clear is that the numbers of people showing up at clinics and through drugs and medical services asking for help, is on the increase.

Experience and effects of heroin

The power of heroin – and that of the other opium derivatives – is to make even the most terrible pain irrelevant and to produce a feeling of tremendous well-being. Some users snort it up their noses, some smoke it, but the most direct rush to the brain comes

Heroin user after 'chasing the dragon'

through injecting. Although most people don't like the thought of putting a needle in a vein, for some dependent users the needle becomes part of the ritual they feel attached to. Apart from that, it is the most economical way to use the drug: the 'hit' is much quicker and the effects last longer. Some people burn it on tin foil and inhale the fumes. This is called 'chasing the dragon' because as the powder burns it curls into a black dragon-like shape. But inevitably, some of the smoke is lost as the heroin burns.

Why is the incidence of death among heroin users so high?

Life expectancy is likely to be reduced for heroin users. Follow-up studies of intravenous drug users show that about fifteen per cent will be expected to die within about ten years of presenting themselves at clinics. Opiates, principally heroin and its substitute methadone are responsible for 2,395 deaths a year in the UK.

Some heroin users share needles and transmit viruses and infections to one another, such as HIV and hepatitis B and C. Heroin deaths are also often caused by accidental overdose. This is often because the drug is 'cut' with other substances so the user doesn't know how much heroin is in the dose and may take too much. There is no way of telling how pure any given batch is. Overdose deaths amongst heroin users can be the result of a burst of really pure heroin hitting the streets. Most is adulterated and so dependent users have become tolerant of the drug in lower doses; an unaccustomed batch of really pure heroin can kill, as it can cause an accidental overdose after a user has grown used to far smaller amounts of heroin. The body can't cope with more than it is used to tolerating.

Mixing heroin with alcohol is extremely dangerous and can cause unconsciousness and vomiting; users sometimes die as a result of vomiting and suffocating whilst unconscious. Death can also be caused by mixing heroin with other drugs such as benzodiazepines. These are legal, over-the-counter tranquillisers much sought after by heroin and other heavy-end drug users because they are suppressants and help them to come down and sleep; heroin users often find that their sleep patterns are seriously disrupted. Benzodiazepines compound the heroin experience because if taken in sufficient quantities, they produce similar effects. The danger is that they can add to the suppressant effect of the heroin and in the worst case, lead to coma and death. When there is no heroin available, heroin users will turn to them to avoid the unpleasantness of withdrawal. The tablets have a sedative effect when taken orally, but some injecting users crush them and liquidise them. This is a very dangerous procedure and can result in blood clotting.

Benzodiazepines are reasonably often to be found in the average bathroom cabinet and parents reading this may well be familiar with them under brand names such as temazepam, oxazepam, alprazolam, diazepam, valium and librium. About a quarter of a million people in the UK are prescribed these pills every year, and there is concern that prescriptions should be reduced because of their dangers. They trade on the street amongst heavy-end drug users at about £1 for three or four diazepam or temazepam.

The lifestyle of heroin users adds to the dangers: they tend to neglect themselves, have poor diets and sad surroundings.

Is heroin addictive?

The simple answer is yes. Given a set of circumstances conducive to dependence, a user will build up physical and psychological tolerance and feel a desperate need for the drug. He or she will need more to get the required state of mind – and then they have become dependent. The word 'addictive' is loaded against the user and the word 'dependent' less weighted down with stigma, which is why it is preferable to talk about dependence rather than addiction.

The problem with opiates is that the dependence is physical as well as psychological. The body builds up a tolerance to them. Someone who becomes dependent – which is by no means an instant occurrence and takes several weeks or even months and some dedication – needs increasing amounts to fulfil heroin's promise of comfort and euphoria.

US soldier in Vietnam

It is difficult to say how many people in the UK are dependent on heroin. Figures for those known to be dependent are based on people who have come up against the authorities through criminal activity, or who have presented themselves at agencies, surgeries or clinics asking for help. There are many other users of whom one hears nothing because their use is controlled. They have jobs, homes and 'normal' lives. They know how to use heroin without it becoming a problem and they do not fit the prejudicial image we have of the street 'junkie': the dishevelled, hollow-eyed, near-death skeletal figure of the 'Heroin Screws You Up' posters.

It is possible for people to use opiates and maintain a habit without getting ill if they have the means to get hold of relatively pure opiates produced in laboratory conditions and their use is carefully controlled. But most users, the ones we know about, depend on the heavily adulterated stuff sold on the streets and manufactured by unscrupulous businessmen bootleggers behind nice clean desks whose aim is merely to make money.

The occasional experimental dose of heroin does not necessarily render you dependent. Research by academic Geoffrey Pearson shows that:

'In some areas when heroin first became available in cheap and plentiful supply, although there might have been a certain degree of experimentation, it did not always catch on . In one locality for example, a group of friends who had an established pattern of recreational drug use involving cannabis and hallucinogens, found that heroin was "too heavy a stone".'

During the war in Vietnam, heroin was easily accessible and very cheap. Many of the GIs used it, whether by injection, snorting or smoking. The heroin they bought was ninety per cent pure, whereas what was available on the streets in the US was only five to ten per cent pure. So what they were getting was likely to give them the best high that heroin can buy. Follow-up studies of these users revealed that of those who were dependent on heroin during their tour of duty, only twenty per cent used it again once they had gone home. Of those, only twelve per cent were dependent and a year later, only one per cent were still dependent.

You might say the Vietnam War can't be compared with the UK in the 1990s. But what the Vietnam GI and the bored, marginalised, disaffected and damaged kid have in common is a desire to escape from their immediate reality. Add to this the sense of hopelessness amongst those young people for whom the future looks bleak and the weird glamour of heroin's status in the realms of rebellion and risk, and you can see the appeal. GIs went home, they left Vietnam behind them, however haunted, hurt or guilt-ridden they were by what they had experienced. Kids without hope locked into heroin on inner-city estates are already at home. Home is part of the problem.

There are two things to unravel from the figures and the experiences of those on heroin. Firstly, heroin is not necessarily addictive. Secondly, the influence of friends on each other, and the setting in which a drug becomes popular (or unpopular), can't be overestimated. This leads to the realisation that in a key way, drug dependence is not just about the drugs themselves, but about all the forces that make up a social environment and influence the destiny of the individual within it.

As we've seen, dependence can be about things that moulded your personality as a child, which is what happened with Johnny whose story I told at the beginning of this chapter. Added to this, heroin and other drugs can become attractive in certain settings and under certain circumstances, and lose that attraction when the setting is removed.

Who is using heroin?

In 1968, doctors in the UK were obliged to notify 'addicts' to the Home Office. This came about in response to the five-fold growth in heroin dependent users being prescribed the drug by doctors. The idea was that by having a list, doctors could ensure that a patient couldn't register with more than one doctor in order to increase his or her dose.

There is no longer an index of addicts by name, but there are fourteen regional databases in England and one each in Scotland and Wales which record numbers of people who ask for help. These are people who come forward for help to surgeries, clinics and agencies; names or personal details are not recorded. Doctors and other medical professionals are not obliged to enter their patients on these databases but many doctors and agencies in fact comply. The latest figure for numbers notified to the databases at the time of writing was 23,313 for the first half of 1996. About half of these are people for whom heroin is their first drug of choice. It is impossible to say how many actual heroin users there are, as those notified to the databases only represent people presenting themselves for treatment. But what should concern parents is that there is a small but significant rise in people under twenty-one notified to the databases with a heroin problem. Doctors almost never prescribe heroin, so the vast majority of those using it are buying it on the criminal networks.

Where does heroin get a grip?

US soldiers in Vietnam eventually went home. Inner city kids already are at home

Young people denied meaningful activity, growing up in areas where there is nothing to do but hang out, without the means to move on, going to overcrowded, over-burdened schools – these are the kids who will be looking for ways to establish their identity, to feel like someone, to achieve some kind of status. For the few, in time-worn ways, gang life and all that goes with it, drugs, alcohol or violence, becomes a way of having an identity, of getting a life.

Social and economic inequalities are at the heart of some of the most serious drug dependence. The reasons why drug dependence is higher in clusters of urban deprivation are complex. It isn't that poverty in itself breeds drug dependence, nor that unemployment does. The kind of place where drugs tend to get a hold are those which have become known as problem areas, like the so called 'sink' estates. The people forced to live in them are those already at the margins of society, who have a multiplicity of problems. Where these problems interlock with all kinds of deprivation, such as bad quality housing, or estates where there is little to do, the interlocking mix promotes both the demand for and the supply of drugs. This is not to blame anyone living in these environments, nor to say that every young person in a problem environment gets into drugs, gangs or crimes. Most don't, but a few do.

Does heroin attract young people?

The Institute for the Study of Drug Dependence (ISDD) points out in its book *Drug Misuse in Britain 1996*:

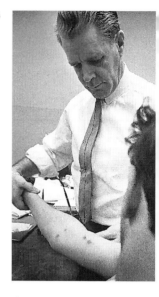

A young user shows the heroin injection tracks on his arm

'... any reasonable estimate would have to leave Britain with an increasing population of mainly young men dependent on heroin, most of whom inject the drug.'

It's clear from all the surveys that other drugs, particularly cannabis, cross age, class, culture and education. Heroin is the exception to this rule. As the *British Crime Survey* of 1996 points out:

'Drug use occurs in all socioeconomic groups, but the use of opiates ... appears to be more frequent in young people who live in poorer and more deprived communities.'

In local areas where heroin gets a grasp, it is often users themselves who deal it for a smallish profit which then funds their own needs. The people who make the big profits never go near the street level dealers. They are often successful criminals who know how to evade the law.

At the time of writing, drugs workers are getting more concerned that heroin is on the increase in its traditional injectable form and also in the form of a powder, known as 'brown', which is being bought by younger kids. This is crumbly stuff that resembles cannabis and is very cheap. Some drugs workers think that kids buy it without realising what it is, thinking the name 'brown' sounds innocent. Nobody knows how much of this is going on, but it is a worrying trend observed by drugs agencies and workers all over the UK. The danger is compounded by the probability that younger people who hang around where drugs are bought and sold are being offered it by people they know and therefore trust, not by spooky strangers.

The insidious and relatively new appearance of this cheap smokable heroin, and other heroin use amongst the young, has been picked up by drugs agencies around the UK. At the Network Drugs Advice Project in Newham, East London, assistant director Colin Cripps has noted an increase. Actual numbers are small, from none under twenty reporting heroin use in 1994 to twelve in 1996. Colin Wisely, director of Unit 51, a drugs agency in Huddersfield, says that the supply lines for heroin are spilling out of inner-city areas and into suburbs like Dewsbury. He is in no doubt that heroin use is on the increase:

'It used to be a rarity for under-twenties to come to us with problems relating to heroin, but now it's commonplace among clients in the sixteen to twenty age range. Heroin is more easily available, it's the overspill from big cities and now even in the villages surrounding Liverpool, Manchester, Leeds and Bradford, you're finding a heroin economy. It's still a very small percentage of younger kids and I wouldn't say it's getting larger, but it's a reflection of the increased use of illegal drugs by young people.'

The news from the agencies is that there is a small number of younger people trying heroin. The message from Mary Smith, whose son is dependent on heroin and who started up KWADS, a drugs help service for parents in Bristol on the Knowle West Estate, is less measured:

'I'd guess that there are 500 people on this estate, out of a population of 20,000, using heroin. I'd say the average age is eighteen, although we had a nine year-old who was picked up by social services and is now in treatment; his parents were drinkers. I'd estimate there are sixty dealers on the estate, all of them people who do it to fund their own habit. It's easy to get heroin now and it's cheap. A gram is £20 and can provide twenty hits.'

In considering how widespread the use of heroin is amongst younger kids, the ISDD concludes that although agencies are seeing younger heroin users:

'... heroin is likely to remain a drug which appeals to only a very small minority of young people. Today's new wave of young drug users overwhelmingly reject its "junkie" connotations.'

Why do some young people develop a habit?

The supposition is that one hit and you're hooked. This is untrue of almost every drug, even crack, whose effects are so powerful but last such a short time that it creates a more rapid craving. Most people who try heroin are sick the first time, and this puts a lot of experimenters off. It's difficult to develop a heroin habit, and it's clear to anyone who goes further than a first time dabble that it carries with it a whole raft of problems that other drugs don't. Someone with hope, things to do, things to look forward to, relationships not exclusively centred on the use of heavy-end drugs such as heroin – such a person isn't likely to become heroin-dependent. Sally Murray, a counsellor at Kaleidoscope, the drug dependence unit in Kingston-upon-Thames, picks up the point about which kids are likely to get into trouble with heavy-end drugs:

'Whether from rich or poor backgrounds, they are almost always people with traumas in their past and for them heroin is very attractive because it's like a warm blanket when you're very cold. It's comforting, it distances reality.'

Risk factors

Jez Buffin, the family worker with drugs agency Lifeline Manchester, sees some 250 families a year and specialises in help for parents and their children under seventeen. He lists the following risk factors for kids who get into heavy-end dependent drug use:

■ They have had periods of homelessness, either because they have run away or been kicked out, before the heroin use began

■ They have lost contact with their biological parents

■ They have become excluded from their non-drug-taking peer groups

■ They often have a background of physical or sexual abuse and a record of emotional problems before their use of drugs began

■ They have been through the youth courts and criminal justice system before starting to use heroin

■ They have been drawn into a peer group using heroin and have become close to people in this group

■ They have been in care.

Most kids who get into trouble with drugs have some of these risk factors in their life story. Not everyone with these risk factors becomes drug dependent, but if a young person's disturbance remains ignored, they may go off the rails in one way or another: problematic drug use is one way.

Isolation, exclusion and acting up
When kids act up, their behaviour makes them unpopular and everyone backs away so they become isolated. Isolation is a feature of the lives of heroin dependent people, as Colin Wisely of Unit 51 explains:

'There is first of all some kind of trauma and the kid acts up. Isolation and exclusion are the key factors in heroin dependency. The acting up leads to exclusion, that exclusion is temporarily alleviated by drugs, but the drugs exacerbate the problem, the young person acts up more and finds himself or herself further excluded and even more isolated. The drug dependence only reinforces the exclusion. They become caught in a downward spiral and their escape routes close off. At the bottom of the spiral there is prison.'

Exclusion from school
Many of the kids Jez Buffin of Lifeline Manchester has worked with have been excluded from school, or have dropped out. There has been no follow-up.

In their report on their work in this field, Lifeline Manchester write:

'When young people lose contact with school and other institutions, they find themselves at high risk of becoming involved with other groups of disaffected individuals whose lives are spent acquiring and using drugs on a daily basis. In fact, of all the many personal and social factors that might be used to predict problem drug use, loss of contact with school is one of the most consistently reliable.'

What can parents do?

Parents of heroin-dependent sons or daughters wish there was some fast track to getting off heroin. It's not usually like that. Heroin users I have spoken to say anyone trying to help them needs to understand that their relationship with heroin is one of love and hate, but that love it or hate it, it has given them a life of sorts.

'Junk is not a kick, but a way of life.'
William Burroughs, author of The Naked Lunch

A day in the life of a heroin user
'Junk is not like alcohol or weed, a means to increased enjoyment of life. Junk is not a kick, but a way of life,' wrote William Burroughs, a novelist famed for his use of drugs. It's difficult for parents of heroin-dependent sons and daughters to understand that although it's not as hard as people think to kick the habit, it's more than the habit we're talking about kicking. For a dependent user, heroin is a way of life.

Heroin-dependent users have a whole lifestyle, a structure that heroin has given them. Heroin has become their friend, their ally, their reason for living, their source of identity. In a curious way, a lot of dependent users have adopted the myth of the junkie who is slave to the substance and the overwhelming need for it. This provides both a sense of meaning – they are involved in something major and serious – and the excuse for not trying to get off the drug. But the drug is also their enemy, their devil, their reason for despair. It's not unlike the relationship a serious nicotine smoker has with cigarettes. Imagine giving up a heavy smoking habit: your life yawns before you as though in a chasm of deprivation, you experience severe withdrawal physically, socially, personally, emotionally – in every way. People say: 'Just stop, just say no, just give up.' But nicotine users know how incredibly difficult it is to give up; and smoking doesn't even blanket out pain or supply you with an entire life structure, as heroin does.

Andy, heroin user, aged twenty-nine: *'I sorted out what got me into being a junkie* when I was in a rehab. I saw my dad killed when I was twelve. He was knocking down the garage and it fell on top of him. I tried to save my dad but he was dead by the time the ambulance arrived. After he died, my mum used to beat me all the time with a belt. I was kicked out of school at thirteen-and-a-half. A teacher drove me home but, when I got there, my bags were packed and outside the door. She comes to the door and says, "I don't want to know you".

'I haven't seen her or my brother since. I went to live in a squat and soon got into a heavy drug scene. Drugs took away the feelings, I used to cry in bed at school but drugs took that sadness away.

'I've been on smack for ten years. It's changed me completely, I'm not sociable, I'm not at all fit, I'm shoplifting and doing burglaries. Of course I wish I'd never got into drugs, and I'd say to kids do yourselves a favour, stay off drugs.'

The heroin-dependent person wakes up and wants the drug. The day begins with schemes to get money, it continues with schemes to get heroin; it can take all day. The heroin user may well have to commit a number of crimes to get the money for the drugs: shoplifting, robberies, breaking into cars. Then he or she seeks out the dealer, usually a heroin user who sells to feed their own habit. The day wears on, the night looms. The user has a little society around him or her, others in the same situation. It's a violent world, and there is little honour among users; instead there is deceit and mistrust born of the savage need for a fix.

Kicking the habit: no quick fix

Parents frightened about their children's heavy-end drug use often hope that they will be given a list of practical things they can do to get their son or daughter off heroin. But there is no quick fix. Jez Buffin of Lifeline Manchester says that what parents need first is to be listened to:

'I've seen parents who had absolutely no idea that their children were using drugs and of course are feeling shocked, devastated and guilty because they think they should have been able to spot it in their children. They want to do something immediately, they think it's like pulling a lever and they'll hit the right combination like a fruit machine, that they'll get the three cherries and everything will be all right. It's not like that, that's the first thing to realise.

'Parents come to see us and they break down, they don't know where to turn or what to do. They have mixed emotions, it's not unusual for them to wish their son or daughter was dead because it would be almost easier to bear. A lot don't even find a way of saying what they're feeling. They don't really want advice at that moment, they just want someone to listen to them. They may not be ready for the advice, they need to vent their emotions and the timing of actually giving out the advice is something we have to be sensitive about. For many of them, how their son or daughter got into heroin is a mystery to them, and it's not the thing they most want to know about – they want to know how to get them out, and not what got them in. We have to be honest about the options that exist and up-front about what they are likely to achieve. We have to say that even if their child goes into a detox and is drug-free for a while, there are no guarantees that that is the end of the matter.'

Finding help and accessing services

There are different sorts of drugs agencies all over the UK.

Sheila, aged fifty, mother of a heroin user:
'**My son was about fifteen** and he got in with this new crowd of boys. We suspected they were taking drugs. They were rough and I didn't want my son going out with them. I became really paranoid, I'd answer the phone and someone would hang up. When he was sixteen or seventeen he got into heroin. At first he sold his own things, then he started stealing jewellery, money, things like videos, from us.

'We never knew where he was. Then he got caught with a stolen car radio, and he was on a police curfew – he had to be home by a certain time as part of his bail conditions. I'd sit by the clock watching the minutes pass. I started going to Families Anonymous. FA helped me understand addiction. I met others through FA, and made some wonderful friends. I tried warning all the families of the other boys he was with about what I suspected they were doing. Some of them didn't care, and after I went to one family, they smashed my husband's car up and threatened to burn down our home.

'And then he was arrested four or five times for stealing from cars and was caught doing burglaries. He was sent to a young offenders institution. There were plenty of drugs in prison. If he hadn't been an addict when he went in, he would have been when he came out. He's been out for a few months now and he's got himself on methadone. He's back living with us. He's waiting for a place on the detoxification unit of a big hospital. This is the best he's been in ten years.

'Drugs are part of young people's fashion. I go round schools speaking to kids now. I also do the FA helpline, it helps me to do these things.'

Jim, Sheila's son:
'I think I was born an
addict. *I was interested*
in money and stealing
which is weird because
I wasn't brought up like
that.

'I had a really good
childhood. I had no need
to blot out any pain, and
I got on really well with
my parents. Most of my
heroin addicted friends
have been kicked out of
home. For some that has
been the kick up the
bum that they needed,
but it doesn't work for
everyone. They end up
somewhere like Kings
Cross selling whatever
they can – themselves –
for drugs, and some I
know have committed
suicide. The main thing
is that parents should
help you. My parents
said to me, "You can't
stay here because
you're stealing from us",
but they sorted me out a
hostel to stay in. I was
hurt and angry at the
time but now I
understand it. They've
stood by me. They've
always said to me, "If
you want help we'll give
it to you, but we won't
give you money so you
can go out and buy
drugs and possibly
overdose".'

To find out places you can go for help in your locality, phone the National Drugs Helpline on 0800 776600, a twenty-four hour a day confidential service.

Be prepared for the possibility that it might be a struggle to find the right place for the help you and your family needs. There is a serious shortage of services for those under eighteen because drugs agencies are mostly dealing with an older age group. You should also be prepared for some drugs agencies to discourage parental involvement. But this is changing and many services now appreciate the needs and the role of parents and cater for them. Parents should ask which agency will be likely to appreciate their involvement when looking for the right sort of help for themselves.

If you want a comprehensive list of agencies all over the UK, get a copy of *Drug Problems, Where To Get Help*, published by SCODA at £5.50; this is currently being rewritten and is due out later in 1997. It is a directory of services all over the UK and Ireland and gives uniquely helpful information. Drug agencies should have copies, but if you want your own, contact SCODA on 0171 928 9500 or at 32 Loman Street, London SE1 0EE.

Cold turkey

Parents want to know what the process of detoxification is, how to get their sons and daughters off heroin, how long it takes – and once they're off, how to keep them off. It's hard for heroin-dependent users to come off on their own without the help of detox units, doctors, agencies or drug dependency units.

The whole idea of 'cold turkey' tends to scare users and their families and friends. But it isn't as bad as its reputation suggests. The last fix wears off a few hours after it's been taken and users become restless and sleepy. Then they get cramps in the stomach, they sweat, their nose and eyes run and they sneeze. Some people have bad diarrhoea. They might shake and tremble, they may feel paranoid and scared, they get goose bumps – hence the phrase 'cold turkey', and their legs twitch – hence the phrase 'kicking the habit'. It's bad, but no worse than really bad 'flu. It can be made easier with the use of certain prescription drugs in medically controlled withdrawal. The worst is over after two or three days, although the after-effects may take a few weeks to wear off completely – like really bad 'flu. People who are dependent will tell themselves the withdrawal is worse than it is – they call it 'clucking'. But they know it's a temporary state and they know it passes. As parents, we can offer to stand by them while they withdraw. We've seen them in every state during their lives and we won't condemn them, however upsetting it is to see anyone you love going through this painful process.

Once through it, what does the user do when the drug is no longer the centre of his or her life? Someone coming off heroin has to find a new life, and most can't just geographically move themselves for a host of reasons, not least of them financial. So don't expect miracles, know that you have to hang on in there and may have to put up with a lot of difficulty before that person is restored to a drug-free state. Michael Gossop, in his book *Living with Drugs*, writes:

'In fact, the addict, like anyone else, faces choices between different options. The decision to give up may be a difficult one. Turning that decision into reality is even more difficult but it is far from impossible and sooner or later most addicts do give up ... drug addiction is far from the irreversible condition that has sometimes been assumed.'

Options for treatment and help
Drug users have different needs when it comes to the actual process of coming off. There's no best or only way. For some, total abstinence is the only way they can imagine kicking their habit. For others, gradual withdrawal is the only way they can imagine of becoming drug-free.

As parents, however frustrated we become by a young user's tendency to relapse after periods of abstinence, we have to try to remember that we are asking a lot of them. It's a major achievement to give up dependence on anything, let alone heroin. We need to be sensitive about not reinforcing any sense of failure, particularly since a sense of failing to be part of the non-drug-dependent world can be one of the things that attracts someone to get into problem drug use in the first place.

Coming off drugs is the first step in a long and hard journey. Heroin users might decide to start the process as a result of an impending court case, or they may be frightened of committing yet another crime to get money for drugs. If this is your son or daughter, and they indicate that you can help, you'll need to be prepared for some dark days and nights sitting it out with them, and as they emerge, helping them to see there is more to life than their love-hate affair with heroin.

Terry, aged fifty, father of a heroin user: *'When my daughter was about fifteen, we never suspected that she was taking drugs, but she was. She was on heroin, I was so shocked I felt like vomiting. I was terribly angry with her. But anger didn't get us anywhere. Children in this situation feel ashamed and guilty. You have to talk to them calmly and rationally or they'll leave, and you'll worry yourself sick.*

We got her into a rehab. I had to tell her to go. It was tough love. We said, "We love you, but we hate what you're doing". She left and went to live in a squat. By the time she was twenty-four, she had reached rock bottom. She was on smack and running out of money to fund it. We got her into an expensive rehab and we take it a day at a time.

'I know now why she might have been vulnerable to drugs. She had a thyroid problem as a child and when she was a teenager she had an operation that left a scar across her throat and one eye enlarged, so she had a lot to go through.'

Do young people's drugs services help young dependent users?

The first step for drug users might be to suggest they go to a drugs agency that will help them. Provision for those aged eighteen and over is relatively easy to find. Young people's specialist drug services are quite scarce but are very helpful to young users.

Many young users may resist making that first visit or call. The reasons they give are:

■ They don't see their personal drug use as a problem

■ They see services as primarily aimed at people with problems

■ They fear the police will be involved

■ There is a stigma attached to being seen to use a drugs service

■ They assume the workers will be, as one teenager put it, 'goody goodies'

■ They imagine drop-in centre staff will be spies for social security

■ Some think that what they tell drugs workers, counsellors and others at drugs services, won't be kept confidential

■ Young black and Asian people may be reluctant to use drugs services because they see them as predominantly white.

By speaking to or visiting the workers at drugs agencies, parents can help to allay their childrens' fears. We can ascertain for ourselves that what our children say will be kept confidential, and not even repeated to us if the young person so wishes. We can tell them that the other fears they have are unfounded.

One of the studies that looked into young people's services found that young people wanted somewhere to go where they could talk to someone who didn't judge them. They talked about:

'... the benefits of being able to "unload" their problems even though solutions were not found. Many of the young people we talked to had experienced disrupted childhoods; it is not surprising that some had come to perceive themselves as a problem, or at the very least, unwanted. Since coming to the [drugs] service, many felt they had started to feel human or a whole person as opposed to just a "drug addict".'

Letting go

Many parents feel they cannot let go of sons and daughters using heroin because they continually blame themselves. But if your son or daughter has become impossible to live with without the rest of the family being torn apart, if parents have done everything they possibly can to help a dependent son or daughter, they should be able to let go at the point where they need to, in order to maintain their own sanity and well-being. As Rosalie Chamberlain, Clinical Services Manager at Kaleidoscope, says:

'Parents often come to see us for help and advice. I have to say that when parents are involved and supportive to their son or daughter who is using, even if the parents are tearing their hair out, it is their children who do better in terms of rehabilitation. A lot of people in trouble with drugs think if their parents don't love them, then nobody does.

'But some parents have lost everything. I had parents in recently whose flat had been burned down by a woman who was a dealer and wanted to get at their son. Even though this had happened, they still supported their son who by then had been arrested, they were standing by him whatever happened although they are having to live in bed and breakfast accommodation.

'I have said that sons and daughters tend to do better when parents remain involved, because they feel they have someone to strive for and have some self-regard because someone else has regard for them. But having said that, there are other parents who come in and want permission to cut loose. I have sympathy for them too. Their sons or daughters have stolen from them, every part of their

lives is affected by the dependence and what it brings with it, and it's very difficult for them to tell their child to go. But at some point, they need to know that having a child isn't a life sentence. It's too easy just to blame the parents and there's a tendency to do that, but if your son our daughter is ruining your life, you shouldn't have to go on indefinitely.'

Options for services and treatment centres

The options for rehabilitation and detoxification are limited, especially for anyone under eighteen. The UK has only a few rehabilitation centres or detoxification beds in units especially set up for the younger dependent drug user: at the time of writing there are only six specialist detoxification beds for people under sixteen. Even where rehabilitation and detoxification services are

Adam, aged forty, former cannabis trafficker and heroin user: '*I started dealing cannabis at school* when I was fifteen. By the time I was seventeen, I had tried coke, smack and LSD and later on I did mushrooms big time to the point that I was loony every day for four months. I did it because of the image, being a hippy was cool. As a cannabis dealer I was somebody. By the time I was twenty-one, I was moving vast amounts. I had some amazing adventures, some real smuggler's tales. Morocco in the 70s was great. We sold it to Moroccan bankers in Agadir, made a fortune, and it was sun, dope, and girls, real debauchery. I was happy as Larry. There was plenty of danger and I loved it. It was like living in a road movie. I never ripped anybody off and had an incredibly good reputation. I was addicted to all of it, the money, the fun and the drugs. I regularly had £200,000 in cash hidden behind walls and in desk tops. We had friends who specialised in passports, specialised cars, that sort of thing. But I deteriorated because I was a closet junkie, I was into smack in a big way but nobody knew. I got to the point where the smack got as dangerous as the contact with the forces of law and order. I remember parking up in a lay-by after an all-night party. I'd had too much heroin and took cocaine to counteract the effect. I passed out and didn't come round until a day later. When things like that started happening, I knew I had to do something. I was on bail at that time and I started going to NA. I handed my life over to God, I was big time into praying. The heroin was killing me, and the cannabis dealing was doing for me as well. I have three kids, they know nothing about my past, nothing at all. I've said to my fifteen year-old, that if he takes drugs, to know that he can always come and tell me and can always ask me for help. But he knows I'd rather he didn't take drugs.'

prepared to take on people under eighteen, it often doesn't help the young person to be in with older people.

An added problem for drugs workers is that there are legal difficulties in treating people under sixteen: under the Children Act, it can be illegal to treat a child without parental consent. But young people's services will not turn away a young person under sixteen. Whether or not they can maintain confidentiality if giving treatment – for example methadone substitution, needle exchanges or condoms – depends on establishing whether or not the young person is responsible enough to understand what they are consenting to, if parents are not there to consent for them.

What follows is an outline of the kinds of services heroin users or their parents might like to know about. These services can help people with other drug problems as well.

Drug dependency units (DDUs)
Most street agencies are in the voluntary sector and funded through a variety of ways. DDUs are mostly in the statutory sector and funded through the NHS. DDUs offer a variety of services and medical treatments, on an in-patient basis and on a drop-in or appointment basis. Through them people can get information, counselling, psychiatric help and detoxification programmes. DDUs will be able to give medical advice and treatment and also offer counselling – a heroin user's problems will not be confined to the drug alone.

Detox and detox units
Some heroin users may have arrived at the point where they are ready for detoxification. It is best to do this under medical supervision. It can be done at home but users and parents are advised to consult a GP who understands the subtleties of drug dependence, or a doctor attached to a local drug dependence unit or street agency. Users may need to have substitute drugs to help them come off; it depends on what they have been using and on their physical and mental state. A few people can kick a heroin habit on their own, but they are rare.

Detoxification units can be effective for some users, but not all; a drugs agency counsellor can help you understand and guide your son or daughter to make the right decisions. Detox units are generally situated in hospitals and clients may be any age, so for a number of reasons, they are not ideal for younger people. On its own, detox rarely seems to provide a user with a long-term solution:

Johnny, heroin user, aged twenty-nine:
'I started sniffing glue when I was eleven, then smoking cannabis when I was fourteen. I wanted to escape from society, because it had nothing to offer. There was nothing to do but hang around the street corners and create havoc. I hardly ever went to school. Then I started going to pubs where I was offered acid and speed, I was a right acid head, I needed nine at a time to get off on them. Then I started taking smack. I'd do speed for ten days then couldn't

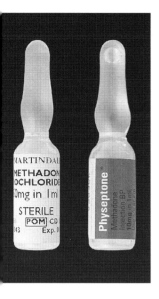

Ampoules of methadone prescribed to heroin dependents

it is most effective when it's done with counselling and follow-up. Waiting lists are long and there are only a few specialist services of this sort.

Methadone substitution

Harm minimisation and prevention go hand in hand with the kind of approach that encourages the use of the drug methadone to help heroin-dependent users come off heroin. The point of getting someone onto a methadone programme is that the substitute drug is less dangerous: it is legally prescribed, it is taken orally and the dose is controlled by a doctor or nurse at a drug dependence unit or other clinic. The idea is to reduce the amount gradually until the user can be weaned altogether. Methadone reduces withdrawal symptoms, but it doesn't produce the 'high' that comes from heroin. Methadone programmes may be administered through DDUs such as Kaleidoscope, where clients visit daily to get their dose.

There are heated arguments about the effectiveness of methadone programmes. Rosalie Chamberlain, the Clinical Services Manager at Kaleidoscope, says:

sleep, so I chased some gear – a bloke in the shared house I was in, he gave me my first hit. I smoked it for a year but then I started banging it up to get the full value.

'These days I can remember things that happened years ago, but ask me about yesterday and I've no idea. Those years on smack were ones of enjoyment and escape, problems didn't mean anything, there was a sense of security. If someone says your house is on fire, you say OK let it burn. But when you've got none, you've

got more enemies than anything else because you feel so sick, you're irritable, nobody will help you. I've been done for shoplifting and burglaries and car theft, I've been done once for carrying a blade.

'I was put in a bail hostel because this policeman came up to me in the street and I said, "I'm not bothering anybody", and this geezer in a suit says, "Nick him", and I said, "Come back and say that again and I'll cut your throat". I got twenty-eight days. I got drugs the first few days.

'As soon as I got out I was back on the smack again. It was a terrible year, I overdosed twice, I wanted to kill myself. I've had a serious think since then. I'm registered at Kaleidoscope for methadone. A junkie's life is disgusting, there's so much lying and deceit amongst users – including myself.'

'Methadone stops drug dependents breaking the law because they get it on prescription and do not have to steal to fund their habit. A lot of heroin is adulterated; because methadone is legal and prescribed, it is not going to be mixed with anything, so they know what they're getting and it's safer. The effects of methadone last on average twenty-four hours, heroin only lasts a few hours, so with methadone you need to take it less often. That gives more stability – they come here to get their methadone once a day and we can monitor their usage. With heroin you're always peaking and troughing, high or withdrawing, but with methadone you're more stable. Because methadone is taken orally, it reduces the risk of blood-borne infection such as HIV, hepatitis B and hepatitis C, which are easily passed on by people using needles.

'Studies at Kaleidoscope have shown a steady decline in the past four years of HIV infection amongst methadone users. Kaleidoscope also give out clean needles and condoms as part of protection against the spread of infection. Our rates of HIV are down: in 1992 we tested 156 clients who were intravenous drug users and 4.1 per cent were HIV positive. In 1996 we tested 196 and only one person was HIV positive, that's 0.5 per cent. We also saw a reduction in people with hepatitis B antibodies in their systems, down from 28.8 per cent to 19.2 per cent. In 1992 we found that sixteen per cent of our clients shared injecting equipment. This has been reduced to thirteen per cent by 1997. The national average is currently twenty per cent. This shows that the combination of easy access to free methadone treatment and syringe and needle exchange works.'

Harm reduction works: giving out needles and condoms and getting people off heroin and onto methadone reduces HIV rates, creates a stabler dependent population and enables them to live a crime-free life. Two studies from the United States show that treatment of dependent users, particularly methadone substitution, is up to seven times more cost-effective than using enforcement to control drug use. Sending people to prison for their drug use doesn't help them and costs more than treatment.

But methadone also has a down side. Some say it is so much less effective than heroin that people 'top up' with other drugs. In the long run, users become dependent on methadone and are therefore still in the dependence trap. It is harder physically to kick a methadone habit than a heroin one. Critics say it is colluding with dependency rather than doing anything to end the cycle.

The death rate amongst heroin users is high, but it was twice as high before methadone became as widely used as it is now. Academics and doctors argue about whether methadone is more dangerous than heroin. But figures suggest that methadone is safer because the *proportion* of overdose deaths amongst methadone users has been considerably reduced, compared to the previous overdose rates amongst heroin users. The actual number of deaths has risen, but so has the number of people using methadone.

Needle and syringe exchanges

It makes sense to accustom ourselves to the notion of harm reduction. One of the initial stages in coming to terms with a heroin-using son or daughter might be to have to confront the reality that they are not only using heroin but are injecting it. They probably won't give up just like that and never return to the drugs – and the needles. For some, part of the affair with heroin centres on the needle: it becomes symbolic of what attracts them to heroin. Leaving it behind is usually a long, slow and difficult process. Resistance to the idea of needles is natural and understandable. But the idea of harm reduction is that the dangers of drug use are minimised by understanding the needs of drug users.

In Edinburgh, where there was little or no access to free needles because of the public unpopularity of needle exchanges, heroin users took needles and syringes from hospital refuse or bought them from other users. In 1987 the incidence of HIV infection had soared to fifty-two per cent among needle-sharing users in Edinburgh. Twenty per cent had shared needles with people in other places apart from Edinburgh. Public pressure against having needle exchanges and similar anti-drugs campaigns backfire: they create increased dangers for drug users and have a knock-on effect on a much wider network of people.

Kaleidoscope runs a needle exchange and free condom service. Over three years they have observed that as a result, the HIV rate has dropped dramatically amongst the people they see. Public concerns are that old needles won't be properly disposed of because of the wild lifestyles of users, but this can be monitored by refusing to hand out new needles unless old ones, carefully logged and registered, are handed back. There is no evidence to show that increasing the availability of free, clean needles increases the risk of intravenous drug use. The needle exchange is often the only point of contact between users and any kind of help and so is a key place for education to begin.

Self help groups

Narcotics Anonymous have groups all over the UK and there is help for families through Families Anonymous. These groups advocate abstinence and members are expected to give up and stay off from the outset of joining. ADFAM National provide information and support for families throughout the country and do not advocate any one basic strategy for giving up drugs. There are also self-help groups like KWADS and Swindon Parents Against Drugs, organisations that can be found through local GP or community networks if they are not listed by a drop-in street agency, library or community centre.

Abstinence

Rather than adopting any one cast-iron approach to rehabilitation, the latest research shows that treatment must be matched to the client. The 'Just Say No' approach has its uses as much as any other kind of treatment. It relates to what is known as the 'disease model': the idea that addiction is a disease and that people are genetically predisposed to it, whether it be an addiction to alcohol or illegal drugs. The problem with this way of seeing it is that the responsibility for the drug use rests with the individual, as if he or she is not affected by history and environment. It simultaneously excuses the individual by saying he or she was born with the problem waiting to happen.

As an idea to start out with – rather than one to use as a tool for rehabilitation – it is full of problems. Professor Griffith Edwards, of the National Addiction Centre at the Maudsley Hospital in London, says there is no such thing as 'the addictive personality'. But for some people with a dependence which they are trying to kick, the idea that they have a disease gives them a straightforward reason for their addiction, and something to fight against.

Concept houses

If someone is lucky, a community care package can be put together for funding in a rehabilitation unit of some kind. Parents should be prepared for bureaucratic difficulties but should push for funding if their son or daughter is eligible, wants to go into a non-statutory rehabilitation centre and can't afford the fees.

The bottom line on entering a concept house is that you stop using drugs forever. Concept houses are rehabilitation centres run on the total abstinence mode. Their regimes are highly structured and those joining them go through group therapy and lectures as well as other kinds of counselling. Counsellors are usually people

Mary, aged fifty-two, mother of a heroin user:
'I was nineteen when I had my son so we grew up together in a way. I tried cannabis in my youth, and I told him about that. I also took speed to lose weight. I sometimes wonder if it affected him. He was addicted for seven years – seven years of hell for us, for him and for the three girls whose lives he ruined. He used his three girlfriends for money, he became so manipulative. The last girl, he took her cash card and got her nicked for shoplifting. He lied, he'd do anything for his next fix but he always worked and kept himself sort of together, he is a painter and decorator for a big firm. But he needed more money than he earns, at one point he had a £500 a week habit. I dread to think how he funded it. He's on the mend now and says he can't believe how he used to use and abuse people.'

who are themselves former heavy-end users of drugs and/or alcohol. For some, this intensive therapy proves too exacting. The theory behind it is that the dependent user, or 'addict' as they would say, takes twelve steps towards a drug free life. This sounds religious: you need to believe in a power greater than yourself which helps to 'restore you to sanity'. The power need not be God, although the twelve steps are presented in a religious way. A term you may hear of is the 'Minnesota method', the name given to the treatment based on the twelve steps.

Therapeutic communities

These are usually fee-paying, but if you think this is what someone needs, there is no harm in making enquiries and finding out if there is a way of getting funding. People stay in these communities, which are drug-free, and follow a tightly structured daily routine. Staff are usually 'addicts' in 'recovery', the idea being that 'once an addict always an addict', but with help an 'addict' goes into remission, hopefully for ever. There is a system of rewards and punishments, and people are expected to look hard at themselves, sometimes in group sessions. The virtue of the approach is that it treats the whole person, not just the drug problem.

Christian houses

These vary but the first condition for entry is that people joining must be drug-free and believe in Jesus as Lord and trust that he will heal them. They do not usually accept lesbians or gay men.

Finding a sense of inclusion

There is no magic cure for drug dependence, and no one philosophy of rehabilitation has been proved more successful than another. It is up to individuals how they respond to treatment or help. But one thing seems crucial: because the dependent user is almost certainly someone who experiences a sense of exclusion and alienation – someone who has few if any allies – finding a sense of inclusion, an ally or allies, is a real basic. A study carried out in 1985 compared two groups undergoing treatment. One group was given a therapist who was cold and mechanical and the other group received treatment from a warm, friendly therapist. The rate of total abstinence three months after treatment was six per cent for the mechanical approach and seventy-three per cent for the warm, friendly one. At the heart of treatment regimes, it is ultimately the relationship with those providing the treatment that is the key. It also appears that people who have long-term treatment as opposed to the short, sharp detox programmes on offer from some units, have better long-term outcomes.

Cocaine

Cocaine, also known as coke, snow or Charlie, is a drug which cuts into several different drug-taking cultures. It has crept into the dance scene but is mostly identified as a rich person's recreational drug and a poor person's treat. I have included it with heroin because it is usually twinned with heroin in the public imagination. This is perhaps because under the Misuse of Drugs Act it is classed in the same bracket as heroin, morphine and the other opiates, although it is a stimulant. I have also put it here because it is estimated to be used by about the same number of people and because of its association with crack, a drug every bit as serious in its implications as heroin, and one that nobody would hesitate to categorise as heavy-end and well beyond the rave.

Cocaine in the usual form of a white powder, commonly sold in a paper wrap

What is cocaine?

Cocaine is a stimulant. Cocaine hydrochloride, to give its full name, usually comes in the form of white, crystalline powder that is carved into 'lines' with a blade. The lines are then snorted up the nose through a crisp rolled bank note. Some habitual users prefer to use tiny spoons which they wear as ornaments around their necks. It can also be smoked or injected.

The experience of cocaine

Cocaine is similar to amphetamine but the experience it buys does not last as long and it is much more expensive. It carries the same risks and dangers as amphetamine. This is a drug that promotes a sense of well-being, mental ability, optimism and energy. It makes people feel confident, excited and exhilarated. Some people find that it turns them on sexually. Users need less sleep and food than usual. Excessive doses can cause anxiety, agitation, a dry mouth, depression, fainting and nausea – and worse. Sniffing produces a milder experience than injecting.

The effects of cocaine

The risks

The occasional recreational user doesn't generally have problems as a result of using cocaine. But the bigger user has problems after coming down from a binge, and users who become obsessed with

Charly, aged forty-six, cocaine dealer: *'I get £600 for an ounce of cocaine. I've been doing it for years. I started taking it when I was twenty, I don't think it's done me any harm, and I'm certainly not dependent. I haven't had a line for six months. It stops me drinking and helps me relax, it makes me communicative and I have a good laugh. I only deal in good stuff, there's a big difference between a good line and a bad line. I buy it from a big dealer, I don't know where he gets it, but I always try it first and he only sells me the good stuff, he says he'll give the inferior stuff to the wallies. Everybody buys it right across the board: working class people, middle class people, rock stars, surgeons, doctors, respectable mothers who say don't tell my husband, and the husband's buying it from me and saying don't tell the wife! I've got two clients in the police force. They are the same people who are picking others up for possession. They say be careful, clean up your flat because they know when things are going down.'*

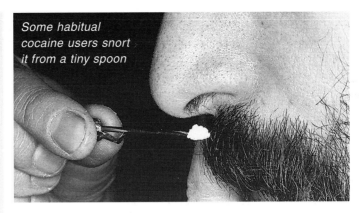

Some habitual cocaine users snort it from a tiny spoon

the drug suffer the consequences physically, psychologically and economically. As one habitual user says:

'Heavy users of cocaine can become psychologically dependent on it and don't want to do anything without the elation they feel when they use it. But heavy users find they can no longer attain the euphoria that got them into it in the first place, and instead they feel anxious, restless and nauseous. And they feel even worse because a really heavy habit could cost £100 a day.'

Giving up a serious cocaine habit, while it isn't easy or pleasant, is not like trying to give up heroin because cocaine users do not have a physical addiction.

As with other street drugs, cocaine users don't necessarily know what they are buying and the drug is probably cut with something else to maximise profits as it passes down the line of dealers until it reaches the street level. In the UK it is not generally cut with harmful stuff.

The most serious physical risks with cocaine come with injecting it. Apart from the other risks associated with injecting drugs – the spread of infection, the danger of abscesses, clotting and damage to the veins – cocaine is dangerous because even a small amount of the drug can result in death if shot directly into the bloodstream. But as the Institute for the Study of Drug Dependency (ISDD) points out:

'Exactly what constitutes a lethal dose of cocaine has not been clearly established: death has been known to occur after injecting as little as 20 mg, whereas one researcher noted the case of a man who regularly smoked 14 grams of freebase [like crack] a day for three weeks.'

People who inject cocaine are usually already using heroin. Mixing drugs in this way is dangerous and the most dangerous way to use cocaine is to mix it with heroin and inject it. This is known as a 'speedball' and is said to increase the feelings of euphoria which each drug on its own can induce. Speedballs can have very serious consequences; according to Andrew Tyler in his book *Street Drugs*, they have caused the greatest proportion of cocaine overdose deaths in the United States. Although the dangers of cocaine should not be underestimated, it is worth pointing out that the actual number of cocaine fatalities is very low: in the years 1985 to 1994 it was implicated in sixty-seven deaths in the UK, the majority caused by mixing the drug with other drugs or alcohol.

Prolonged use by snorting can damage the membranes that line the inside of the nose. Ultimately surgery may be required, but this is rare. People who smoke cocaine heavily and for prolonged periods can expect to have the respiratory problems associated with smoking.

Are young people using cocaine?

According to the ISDD, less than one per cent of the population is likely to have tried cocaine. In a survey carried out by the Health

Sarah, aged sixteen, polydrug user (a user of many drugs):
'*I moved away from my mum's years ago*, and then my dad's. Then I was in care and eventually fostered. I've been taking drugs since I was twelve. I lived with my mum until I was fourteen, she was pimping me to older men. She always used to hit me from when I can remember. She used to take me away on foreign holidays. She would book me into my own room in hotels and by the end of the evening she had found a "partner" for me to spend the night with. She told me what made men feel nice. I would do anything to make my mum happy. She would leave me alone for whole weekends at a time. She left me food and money for shopping. Then when I was fourteen, I got a bad school report and she beat me up and kicked me out. I went to my dad's, but I didn't get on with my stepmother and she threw me out. My best friend's mum took me in and said I needed a social worker so I got one, she's nice, she helps me.

'I do loads of different drugs, E, speed, LSD, cocaine. I get a lot of cocaine through my boyfriend who's in the music business. I feel suicidal quite a lot. I've tried to kill myself four or five times and been taken to casualty. My mum was called by the hospitals I was taken to, but she only came once for five minutes. She made me go with between thirty-five to forty men, and it hurt. The

Education Authority of over 11,000 school pupils aged nine to fifteen, only one per cent or less had tried cocaine, heroin or crack; however, on the basis of other surveys the ISDD says about four per cent of young people may have tried cocaine. Surveys of heavy-end users show that heroin users also use cocaine and crack, but this is not their preferred drug. Problematic cocaine users are usually the same people as problematic heroin users: a small number of people, and an even smaller number of teenagers.

Cocaine has never really caught on with young British drug users. Those few teenagers who do use it probably either smoke or snort it as a 'special treat'. It is too expensive and amphetamine remains a more attractive option because it is cheaper and its effects, which are similar, last a lot longer.

Cocaine psychosis

Cocaine can cause a kind of psychosis like amphetamine. People suffering from this become paranoid and delusional as with amphetamine (see page 91). But once they have given up using cocaine and it is out of their systems, these people will return to their usual state of mind: the damage is not permanent. Recovery can be quite rapid – a matter of weeks – although for some people it takes a few months to feel really well again.

oldest was sixty-two, I was thirteen. I said to my mum, "I'm only doing this to make you happy", and she said, "That's not true – you like it".

'I don't think anyone believes me about my mum because she's elegant, well-spoken, and smart looking. I haven't lived with her for the last two years, and at the moment I'm in foster care. I'm having counselling which is helping me to cut down on drugs.'

The most common use of cocaine is not excessive or damaging. Most users are casual and recreational and have no problems, a few are bingers and the exceptional few are those for whom compulsive use leads to serious problems. But as one seasoned cocaine user says, it doesn't always bring out the best in people:

'People who are ill at ease with themselves sometimes clutch on to cocaine, and blame it for all their problems. It's much easier than asking themselves what might really be wrong. Heavy cocaine use is often a secret shared by a tight group of people who provide each other with a strong identity in being members of such a set. Puffed up on an artificial high and proud to be spending huge sums, such a scene is a magnet for the arrogant and the desperate. And excessive use will end up making takers edgy and paranoid whenever they are not on the stuff.'

A brief history of cocaine

Cocaine is derived from the coca plant which grows in Central and South America. From the thirteenth to the sixteenth century, it was thought of as a gift from the sun god and used almost exclusively by the ruling classes. By the sixteenth century it had become clear that miners in the newly colonised Peru worked harder while under the influence of the coca leaf, and needed less food to keep them going. Added to that, the churches made money out of tithes on coca.

Coca is said to be rich in essential vitamins and if chewed in leaf form and in reasonable moderation, causes no harm to the user. It found its way to Europe in the nineteenth century when German scientists extracted cocaine from the coca plant for medical use. In its early days in Europe, cocaine was popular with the psychoanalyst Sigmund Freud who at first said of it that it provided '... exhilaration and lasting euphoria ... [which] in no way differs from the normal euphoria in a healthy person ... this result is enjoyed without any of the unpleasant after effects that follow exhilaration brought about by alcohol'. In later years he was to revise his opinion and left out any reference to his involvement with the drug when he wrote his autobiography.

Cocaine was so popular in the late nineteenth century in the United States and some European countries that it was sold in cigarettes, soft drinks, nose sprays and chewing gum. Pure cocaine could be bought over the counter in chemist's shops. A Corsican chemist called Angelo Mariani even made wine with coca in it. This proved to be popular with all sorts of notables at the time, amongst them the Czar of Russia, the Prince of Wales, and most surprisingly, the

Cocaine provided psychoanalyst Sigmund Freud with exhilaration and euphoria

Pope, who gave its inventor a medal for his beneficent deeds for humanity. It proved profitable for the manufacturers of medicines who marketed it as a cure for all manner of ailments. One famous product was Ryno's 'Hay Fever 'n' Cattarrh Remedy' which was 99.95 per cent pure cocaine. In 1885 Coca Cola was introduced in the USA, containing a combination of two drugs, caffeine and coca; the coca wasn't removed until 1906.

In the late nineteenth century, coca was used to treat hysteria, whooping cough, sore nipples, digestive disorders, syphilis and asthma. These were times when the causes of illnesses were more problematic to treat than the symptoms, so drugs like cocaine and morphine which gave relief from pain and discomfort were welcomed.

In the early part of the twentieth century, it became clear that there were problems in using coca in medicine and it began to fall out of favour when patients became dependent on it. By 1932 in the United States there were laws restricting its use and sale and all but two states had outlawed unauthorised possession. In the UK during World War One, it was claimed that prostitutes were selling cocaine to soldiers on leave and this was thought to be a German plot to destroy the British Empire. It became illegal to possess cocaine or opium unless you were a doctor, pharmacist or vet. In the UK in the 1970s cocaine was popular with rock stars, high fliers, movers and shakers: the jet setters who could afford it. For some it proved a problem as they found its dangerous charm irresistible. In the 1980s, still carrying an aura of glamour, cocaine became popular with 'yuppies' and tales of its infiltration into high pressure jobs were common. There is no reason to believe that it is any less popular now with those able to afford it.

Crack

Cocaine's reputation as a serious and dangerous drug is probably these days largely due to crack, a cocaine derivative for which major claims of destructive, addictive power have been made.

What is crack?

Before crack there was freebase, a form of cocaine which has been treated in such a way as to maximise its potency way beyond the power of ordinary cocaine. Crack is much the same as freebase, and is so called because of the crackling sound it makes when it is being burned.

It comes in the form of crystals known as rocks. The rocks are heated up either in a makeshift crack pipe made of old tin cans or empty plastic bottles, or is heated on tin foil and the vapours inhaled.

Is crack addictive?

Crack has been described in newspapers and TV programmes as the ultimate 'one-hit-and-you're-hooked' drug, fuelling stories of whole areas of North American cities which are no-go areas for anyone but the crack dealer and the crack user. There is some truth in some of these stories, but the scare factor as translated into the UK drugs scene has to be set in perspective. The idea that crack

Sam, aged thirty-eight, crack user: *'I'll tell you something about crack. I went to parties where everyone was doing it – top end, glamorous people, really smart and then the bottom end, the derelict buildings. I sold everything I owned to get crack. I took a hard look at myself one day and thought I'd better stop. I got to the stage where I wanted the crack so badly I would crawl on the floor for crumbs, it made me feel so alert, like I was the best person in the world and the world is a good place – for three minutes – and then you have to have more. I'd come down from it crying and feeling terribly lonely.*

'I went to jail and my probation officer got me into a rehab. It took me two years to pick myself up again. If someone offered me crack now I'd be really tempted so I'm not going to put myself in situations where that could happen. I've enrolled in college and I'm doing voluntary work. My girlfriend visited me in the rehab and she says she wants me back. It's been eight months since I had drugs. I hope it will last the rest of my life.'

hooks you after one try is dismissed authoritatively by a government sponsored survey, which concluded:

'Only a very few people we spoke to had regularly used crack, with many having tried it once before. Many of these young people reported that they had not found crack to be as instantly addictive as it is often claimed to be by the media.'

The people they spoke to during their research were already seeking help with other drug problems. It is of some comfort to assume that if these people – people familiar with many drugs – found crack to be less addictive than the media would have us believe, then the young people for whom drugs are a relatively unproblematic feature of their culture would find it even less attractive.

But Tim Bottomley of the Trafford Piper Project says that someone who already has the risk factors in their life that can lead to dependence can build up a psychological need for crack. It is the only drug which can make a person spend £1,500 a week – the hit is so intense, the feelings so powerful. But this desperate state remains the preserve of a few. Bottomley says that in the United States crack peaked in the mid 1980s. Since the start of the 1990s, it has decreased every year except in certain parts of some of the inner cities among 'people with little to lose who are least able to cope'. The person most likely to fall foul of crack and build up a habit will once again be someone already at risk before encountering the drug. As researcher Yvonne Pearson writes:

Crack smoking in New York

'Crack is seen by young people as being dangerous and most choose not to use it. They would choose cannabis, ecstasy or a dab of cocaine for luxury. The ones who move into crack are those who are already vulnerable, the ones who are already at risk.'

Is crack use widespread in the UK?

When crack first made its way over the Atlantic, a US Drugs Enforcement Agency officer called Robert Stutman told British police chiefs in 1989 that they should be prepared for a crack onslaught similar to that in some of the US inner cities where the crack scene had taken hold of sections of ghetto communities with devastating effects. A special police crack team was set up, but because the American experience didn't materialise in the same way in the UK, it has since been disbanded.

Crack made the usual kind of British headlines and provided us with something to be terrified of once again. Crack is a fearsome drug because it is very powerful. Because it is so profitable and potentially dangerous for the user, it can get a grip on an area and make life very hard for people in the crack culture and anyone else around them. But it isn't widespread. Crack gets a hold in places where unemployment is high and prospects low. It is cheap to make, easy to sell and seductive to the user. It makes an alternative economy in places where people are hard-up and marginalised. But it doesn't exist in all such environments by any stretch of the

Crack is an inner city problem. A vandalized housing estate in Kirkby near Liverpool

Janet, aged seventy-five, lives on an East London estate with a crack house next door: *'It used to be so nice, so quiet here.* Then three years ago I got some new neighbours and they are involved in drugs. For the last three years it's been terrible. I rang the council but they did nothing. Then one night, one of the sons in there went berserk and did £2,500 worth of damage. I rang the police and the boy threatened me. He would regularly go berserk, throw furniture out of the windows, I was terrified. The music blows the ceiling off. They are dealing crack twenty-four hours a day.

'Prostitutes go in and out. It's a crack house and a brothel. There's a new big bloke running the place, the police told me he was up in court for cutting a man's throat but the main witness was too frightened to appear against him. I was mugged coming in one evening and they caught the man, he had a crack pipe in his bag. I was badly bruised and taken to hospital in an ambulance. I have to take nerve tablets now.'

imagination. It exists in pockets of inner-city areas where drugs already have a grip, and where there is a ready market for it. It is found in parts of London, Greater Manchester, Merseyside, the West and East Midlands and Bristol. Although it will have reached other places as well, it remains almost exclusively an inner-city phenomenon.

The nature of crack use means that if for no other reasons, the financial aspect will exclude very young users from getting into crack problems. Mark Gilman of Lifeline Manchester says:

'Most kids haven't got the money for crack, and it's not a recreational drug. The only kids I've met who are using crack are a very small number of young people already living deviant, disenfranchised life styles and are already using heroin or methadone before they get into crack. They are people with a lot of problems, they are isolated, they are a small minority. They have usually tried heroin first, although for some, crack is the route to heroin because they get almost psychotic with anxiety after a while on crack and need a depressant to bring them down – and that's what heroin does for them.'

Crack is often associated in the public minds with the African Caribbean community. Harry Shapiro of the ISDD has written:

'Crack may be used more widely in these areas but even here, most crack users are white. Variations in the racial mix of users may reflect the location and connections of Jamaican crack traffickers rather than any propensity for black people to use crack.'

It is a serious mistake to scapegoat black communities, especially since, as Shapiro points out: 'Police and drug workers also acknowledge the involvement of Asian and white dealers: they tend to be more discreet in their dealing and so are likely to have a lower public and police profile than their black counterparts.' And any idea that black teenagers are more likely to be using drugs than their white counterparts is entirely wrong. Surveys show that if anything, a smaller percentage of sixteen to twenty-nine year-olds from the black and Asian communities are using or trying drugs.

Just to confuse everyone, in direct contradiction to other findings, researcher Yvonne Pearson observes something quite different. In her research into Nottingham's Crack Awareness Team (CAT) in the mid 1990s, she found that the majority of the clients were from the black community. She also observed that most were not polydrug users (users of many drugs), but crack was their first problem drug. It's hard to say what this might mean for the rest of the country. It might mean that CAT, a unique twenty-four hour rapid response service, has reached crack users that other agencies or researchers haven't reached by employing the services of local people who could penetrate the crack world without causing suspicion or hostility.

At the moment nothing is conclusive, but crack dependence is almost certainly largely the preserve of an unfortunate few for whom a complex web of antecedents and risk factors has led them there.

Louise Clark, the women and crack development worker at Network Drugs Advice Project, has encountered very different kinds of people with crack habits:

'It's an equal opportunities drug, it's just that it's associated with poverty because it's more visible in the working class areas where people feel they have nothing to lose. It's getting there in suburbia. There are stockbrokers coming in in Land Rovers and going home and piping it, the dealers are selling to them, we hear it from the dealers and the users. I have worked with lawyers with crack problems. It's difficult for them to come into a drugs project like this.

'And it's hard to help the prostitutes who are in the crack houses twenty-four hours a day, seven days a week, fifty-two weeks a year. Where are they meant to go? I would like to see a safe house for these women, I could fill several houses. Drugs services have nothing to offer them. There are only three women-only rehabs in the UK, one is always full, another is run by a man who doesn't

Tina, aged eighteen, a raver: *'Hard core went out and jungle music came in and although I've always taken E and speed, and I've tried cocaine in a spliff, I don't like that scene. There are people on crack at jungle raves, it's boys take it mostly, and OK, they don't have enough money to get really fucked up on it, and there's no one-off addiction, but I've heard them say they feel so shitty the next day, they just want more of it but it's so expensive they wait until the next big night out. I'd never ever do crack, no way, it's too scary. It has a scummy image – skinny prostitutes and heavy dealers, scary men: you see them in one bit of the area I live in.'*

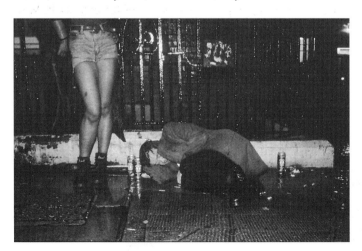

King's Cross, London: the drug services have nothing to offer the prostitutes in the crack houses

Paul, polydrug user and dealer: *'I was brought up dead strict*, my dad would say, "Rock this boat and you're in the water, I'm the captain of the ship". My mum was my idol, I worshipped her and I was always her baby, being the youngest. I used to get beaten if I wasn't in by nine p.m. I started with a bit of puff to be like my mates. I was about thirteen. My parents didn't know about the drugs. I started selling puff when I left school and got an apprenticeship. I failed my apprenticeship and went into selling drugs full time. Then I started selling coke because it was more profitable. Soon I had a brand new Astra. Then I got a prison sentence when I was nineteen. My mum died while I was in there and my dad had died three years before. It really cut me up. When I came out I started dealing crack. Then my girlfriend had a baby and I loved him a lot. But by then I was heavily dependent on crack and she left me which made me wallow in self-pity. Once you're addicted to crack you'd steal from your own doorstep.'

like lesbians or gays, and the other is only open from nine to five. The domestic violence refuges don't let in women on drugs, specially not crack users. There is a growing and significant number of people, women amongst them, who are using crack, and women are in more trouble because the system is geared towards white male opiate users. The safest place for these crack-using women in trouble is prison.'

There are other crack users, the ones we don't generally hear about, who use it recreationally. These users generally have something to focus on that discourages them from getting into the dangers of dependence and need. They have jobs, sturdy relationships or families. But little is known about them as they don't come into contact with drugs services or GPs, so the users we hear about are the few for whom the crack compulsion has become really serious.

The experience and effects of crack

Crack gives the user an almost instantaneous hit and a tremendous sense of power, confidence and excitement. Lifeline Manchester's Director of Research, Mark Gilman, says:

'It is the most powerful pharmaceutical stimulant any society has ever had. It turns a geek into a Cantona. Someone who's always thought of himself or herself as nobody, says "I've arrived! This is the real me!". But that's a terrible lie.'

As with all drugs, what happens to someone trying it depends on the individual, the reasons for using it, the situation in which the drug is used and the quality and power of the drug itself. Most young people who try crack – and according to research very few do – try it once or twice and realise it's not something you trifle with. The problem with crack is that the high is so rapid, but it only lasts a matter of ten minutes or so. Each hit can cost around £20 so someone who has a crack dependence will need hundreds of pounds a week to stay on it.

Crack smoking is very damaging to the lungs and can cause serious chest pains, bronchitis and asthma. Babies born to women who used crack during pregnancy show symptoms of withdrawal in the days after they are born. The lifestyle of the crack dependent user is associated with violence and squalor. Crack users tend also to use heroin and benzodiazepines to deal with the agitated crash when the drug's effects wear off.

What can parents do?

Bob Gilman of Lifeline Manchester says:

'My advice to parents is to keep lines of communication open and watch for kids drifting into isolation unknowingly. The effects of cocaine and crack aren't as well known as the other drugs. Cocaine is insidious, it's creeping into the dance scene, and in my personal opinion, I think parents should know about the subtleties of how these drugs get into their kids' subculture.'

He says cocaine has crept into the rougher edges of the dance scene in clubs where the love ethos of ecstasy has given way to something more aggressive and violent. He is concerned that there is a relationship between cocaine, a drug he sees as dangerous enough, and slipping into crack, cocaine's rougher and more powerful derivative:

'Cocaine has the power to turn people into egomaniacs and it goes back to the days before ecstasy when blokes would have two pints, a curry and a punch-up. The danger is that if someone gets accustomed to the powers of cocaine, and then there is a sudden drought, which happens with cocaine outside London, there is always crack. That's because it is relatively easy and very profitable to turn cocaine into crack. So a young person in a club might find that in the absence of cocaine, he'll be offered crack and try it. That's worrying.'

Parents can try to explain what Gilman says about crack filling a demand for cocaine in its absence, that when it's not available someone may try to sell them crack. They might try it one weekend for fun, and find that the following weekend the cocaine is still not around, and try the crack again. After a few weeks they might find they are craving it. They may not be aware of the difference between the powder, which provides less of a rush and a less intense craving for more, and the crack whose intensity builds up a strong desire for more, especially if that person is already suggestible, unstable or in need of an escape most would neither pursue nor need. Parents can appeal to their children's intelligence by explaining the power of crack to wreck a life, an approach that may be more effective than a straightforward ban.

If a parent reading this book has a son or daughter who is using crack, as with any other drug, keep the lines of communication open. Try not to panic. Find out as much as you can about it, talk

Sally, aged eighteen, former crack and heroin user: *'I was brought up in care. I ran away from my foster parents when I was thirteen. I got in with some wild girls. They were doing all sorts of drugs and soon I started getting money the way they did: prostitution. And then along comes a pimp and says they're your friend, they take you to a nice flat and treat you like a queen and then turn nasty and beat you up unless you go out to earn your keep. They keep the money and get you on crack so you'll do anything for your next hit. It made me feel nothing could ever get to me again – as long as I had it all the time. The crack scene is awful, when it runs out people start attacking each other for more. Then I got onto heroin. In the end I decided I'd had enough of the rough edge of the world. I went to a drugs agency and they helped me a lot. Now I'm on a methadone programme and I'm coming through, I'm in love with a bloke and we want to have a baby. I'm lucky, I'm the one that got away.'*

to other parents, contact local drugs services, see if your GP has any advice to offer. There are specific things parents need to be aware of in relation to crack and the Piper Project have produced a leaflet on crack for friends and families of crack users. They make the points that:

■ Crack can be a very problematic drug but your child's use may be temporary and experimental

■ Don't deal with this on your own, seek help

■ Don't be too soft: crack uses money like no other drug, so don't be scared to say no when asked for more money than usual

■ Don't be surprised if they don't want to talk to you about it, it may be easier for them to talk to a professional, someone at a remove

■ Be patient: they may come down from a crack high and say the kinds of things we say after a hangover – 'I'll never drink again' – followed by the return to a drink for the 'hair of the dog' treatment. A crack user may come down badly and say they'll never do it again, but may return to it

■ Talk to the person using drugs, let them know that you are prepared to help them but that they need to help themselves; you can't get them to stop taking it, they have to do it

■ Crack users can become agitated and aggressive, so wait until they calm down before trying to speak to them about their drug use.

Before doing anything, a worried parent would be well advised to find out what local drug services have to offer a crack user. There is no substitution programme as there is with methadone and heroin. In fact, crack users sometimes go onto heroin as a way of mellowing out from crack's agitated high. Agencies can prescribe beta blockers to help stabilise moods. Some agencies provide acupuncture and Harry Shapiro of ISDD reports that this has been found very helpful in reducing the crack craving. Research by Yvonne Pearson in Nottingham concluded that for a heavy-end crack user, 'abstinence-orientated counselling and support, usually in a residential setting, offers the best treatment prospects'. Although such services remain scarce, particularly for people under eighteen, if parents come to the conclusion that this is what is needed and their children respond to this need, local agencies can tell them how to go about getting them. Agencies are becoming increasingly aware that for a crack user, waiting lists and referrals for future appointments aren't what they want: they want help on the spot. A concerned parent needs to know if that is available.

Something Pearson observed was that crack users often don't perceive of themselves as having a problem. She writes:

'Denial remains strong with crack. This could be partly due to the psychological nature of the dependence and the absence of acute physical withdrawal symptoms. Consequently, the immediate problem which clients frequently faced was their inability to pay. Those who could afford to fund habits in excess of £1,000 a week often did not believe themselves to have any problems. At high levels of usage, individuals became aggressive and dangerous yet remained utterly fixed in their belief that their crack consumption was not the problem. Meanwhile families became scared and helpless when faced with angry denials.'

The rare but unfortunate family which finds itself in this situation needs advice on how to react to the son or daughter whose crack use has led to aggression. Don't suffer it alone: agencies will not report users to the police, but will help family members to consider what, in their particular circumstances, would be the best approach.

Keith, crack user: *'I'm in a rehab now and trying to get off drugs altogether. The crack scene is very, very heavy. One place I used to buy from, the minders had guns. The people using crack were mainly prostitutes, drug dealers and criminals. You go in and there's a group of people smoking crack using pipes made of plastic bottles or glasses. I only did it in a binge sort of way: I'd have a lot and then not have any for a while. But I understand the compulsion and I know people who devoted their entire lives to funding their habits and getting the drugs. I would try and dissuade anyone from ever trying it, it ruins lives.'*

Chapter Six

Smoke and drink:

Tobacco and alcohol

In our obsession with illegal drugs, we tend to forget the abuse, misuse, dependence, problems and ill health caused by the legal ones: tobacco and alcohol. We accept, tolerate and even glamorise them. These drugs are almost completely tolerated by older generations who can't tolerate the recreational polydrug experimentation of their teenaged sons and daughters.

The mass popularity of illicit drug experimentation amongst our children has frightened, perplexed and upset us, not without reason. That's why this book has attempted to shake down some of the myths, present some of the facts and look at ways of dealing with drugs, remembering always that they are not an isolated phenomenon but are intertwined with many other aspects of our lives.

Research shows that young drug users are also likely to smoke tobacco and drink alcohol. The facts in relation to smoking and drinking alcohol speak for themselves.

Tobacco

Tobacco is the only legally available consumer product which kills people when it is used entirely as intended. Tobacco smoke contains over 4,000 different chemicals, many of which are harmful. Each cigarette smoked is a legalised cocktail of lethal substances. Nicotine, carbon monoxide and tar are three components of this smoke which affect our bodies and cause diseases. It is easy to build up a dependence on nicotine. Young people who smoke risk developing a dependency that can last a lifetime, make them ill and cost them a fortune. Yet everyone knows how difficult it is to give up. The risks are immediate for minor illnesses; and as time passes, smokers put themselves at increasing risk of illness later in their lives.

Tobacco: the hard facts

■ 120,000 smokers in the UK die every year as a result of their habit

■ Smoking kills six times more people in the UK than road and other accidents, murder, manslaughter, suicide, illegal drugs and AIDS all put together

■ About half of all smokers will eventually be killed by their habit

■ Eighty-one per cent of deaths from lung cancer are caused by smoking

■ The younger people start, the more they smoke; and the longer they carry on, the greater the risk

■ The risk of dying from coronary heart disease is two-and-a-half times greater in smokers and three-and-a-half times greater in heavy smokers

■ Seventy-six per cent of deaths from chronic bronchitis, emphysema and related disease are smoking-related

■ Most adult smokers started before they were eighteen.

120,000 smokers die in the UK every year as a result of their habit

How many young people are smoking?

In 1994, twenty-six per cent of fifteen year-old boys and thirty per cent of fifteen year-old girls were found to be regular smokers, despite the fact that it is illegal to sell cigarettes to anyone under sixteen. The figure for younger children, those between eleven and fifteen, is twelve per cent, a slight rise in the 1990s. And yet amongst adults, the rate is decreasing. ASH, the anti-smoking pressure group, points out:

'We think it is advertising and promotional materials which affect and influence younger smokers. The tobacco industry needs 300 new smokers a day just to keep level and to replace the smokers who die.'

The tobacco industry spends an estimated £100 million per year on advertising and the government earns some £9 billion per year on tobacco duties. The myths about drug pushers at the school gates – in fact most young people swap and buy illegal drugs amongst each other – really do apply to this massively profitable legalised pushing of a highly addictive drug: nicotine.

The effect of parental smoking on young people

Studies show that children who smoke are likely to have parents or siblings who smoke. The attitude of parents, whether they are smokers or not, plays a key role in children's smoking habits. If children think parents will not disapprove, they are more likely to become smokers. In the case of smoking, 'Do as I say and not as I do' is the best line for a parent who can't give up smoking. Attitude is the key: parents can admit that while saying something sensible – 'Don't smoke' – they are doing something stupid themselves, and that they are not proud of it.

How many young people are drinking alcohol?

Lots. Government figures show that young people are starting to drink at an earlier age and that they are drinking more heavily. A study from Manchester University's Alcohol and Offending Research Project found that amongst their sample of fourteen and fifteen year-olds in eight schools:

- Eighty-six per cent were current drinkers

- Half of them said they drank with their friends and just under half with their parents

- Sixty-five per cent said they had been very drunk at least once in the last year and ten per cent got drunk once a week

- Most said they drank for fun, to celebrate birthdays and Christmas and similar events, and twenty per cent said they did it because they were bored.

Health and accident hazards

We tend to underestimate the dangers connected with alcohol. Alcohol is a contributory factor in twenty to thirty per cent of all accidents, and accidents are the biggest cause of death amongst people under thirty. Here are some other facts:

- 1,000 people under fifteen are admitted to hospital every year with acute alcohol poisoning

- Alcohol is associated with numerous illnesses and is involved in some 28,000 deaths a year

- Eighteen to twenty-four year-olds have the highest consumption of drinking at unsafe levels.

If the smoking and death threats carry little weight with young people, who feel they will live forever and never get old, parents can appeal to their desire to remain youthful and impress upon them that smoking will in fact make them look old before their time. Smoking dehydrates the skin, causes premature wrinkling and makes skin lack-lustre and grey looking. It's also worth pointing out that if you give up while you are still young, your body will return to a healthy state because the damage will only have been temporary – but this means giving up pretty soon after starting.

Passive smoking

It obviously helps to promote the idea that smoking tobacco is not a good thing if parents themselves do not smoke, particularly if they are determined to prevent their children experimenting with cannabis which is usually smoked with tobacco. But if parents do smoke, they could get their children to remind them that passive smokers – the people breathing in smokers' fumes whilst not themselves smoking – have an increased risk of getting smoking-related diseases. We wouldn't knowingly pour small amounts of poison into the food we prepare for our children unless we were insane, but in effect we are pouring small amounts of poison into the air they breathe when we smoke and either ignoring the consequences or justifying it. With that kind of mass hypocrisy, how can we expect to discourage our children from using illegal drugs which arguably do a lot less damage?

Alcohol

Alcohol is increasingly popular with young people

Despite being the world's second biggest killer in terms of drugs after tobacco, alcohol is legal and easily available and statistics show that it is increasingly popular with young

people. Under the law, a fourteen year-old can go into licensed premises, although they can't drink alcohol. At sixteen it is legal for them to buy beer, port, cider or perry but not spirits, if they are in a licensed place and also having a meal. If they drink anywhere else, it is legal unless they are under five. Once they reach eighteen, it is common for the majority of young people to drink regularly not just for pleasure but also because it marks the crossover into adult life.

Alcohol and anti-social behaviour

In the Manchester study, eighty per cent of the young people questioned said they had been anti-social as a result of alcohol, through making a racket in the street, petty offences such as vandalism, or more serious offences of theft and car-related crime. Thirty per cent reported fighting and about the same number admitted to stealing from home or shoplifting. Half of the incidents of disorderly behaviour occur shortly after pub closing time, particularly on Friday and Saturday nights, and often involve young men.

It seems only a matter of common sense to look at these figures and see that alcohol has a really startling effect on our children. And yet we are so much more alarmed by the idea of them taking an illegal drug. Since the most commonly used illegal drug is cannabis it's worth pondering on the idea that there are no such people as cannabis louts, and that it's more or less unheard of for groups of teenagers to get rowdy in the streets, wreck bus shelters, nick supermarket trolleys, break into cars and shoplift after smoking it.

That's the alcohol horror story. Drinking in moderation, sticking to the advisable limits of a three unit maximum per day for adult men, and two units a day for adult women, poses no significant health risks. But these units cannot be applied to teenagers who haven't reached physical maturity. For them, the occasional 'ceremonial' drink of a lighter form of alcohol (not spirits) in small quantities, will do them no harm.

As parents we have to be straight about our own alcohol and tobacco consumption and to understand that if our kids compare our alcohol use with their drug use, they have a point. Denying that there is a comparison will decrease their trust in us because they know there are legitimate comparisons to be made.

Chapter Seven

Drugs and the law

Parents contacting drugs advice lines and agencies often ask whether their children are going to get into trouble with the law. It's only natural that this should be a major worry, because drugs are illegal and having almost anything to do with them is in itself an illegal act. Many parents will therefore naturally make an immediate equation that drugs = trouble = police = punishment = disaster.

In a way, they are right. But to get it into perspective, most who are caught are cautioned and a small number are fined, given community service orders, probation or supervision orders or given absolute or conditional discharge. Only a tiny fraction of drug offenders under twenty-one go to prison: one per cent of people under seventeen and three per cent of people aged between seventeen and twenty-one.

The majority of drug offences committed by people under twenty-five, for which they are found guilty and dealt with by the police and courts, are to do with the possession of cannabis.

But there's no room for complacency. Getting caught with illegal drugs can be very serious. And any contact with the law is frightening for the young person involved and for parents, carers and guardians.

Most parents will try to dissuade their children from having anything to do with drugs and will go for the 'Just Say No' option. But this may not be realistic. Sons and daughters may insist that they will say no, they may intend to say no, but they may find that in reality they are tempted to experiment and say yes, or are already using drugs and not telling their parents.

So what can parents do to help them? In order to reduce the possible dangers and the harm that may be done by being caught with drugs, it is important to have a working knowledge of how the law works and what to expect.

Drug laws

The most commonly used law controlling drugs is the Misuse of Drugs Act 1971 (MDA). The aim of the act is to stop the abuse of certain controlled drugs without stopping their correct medicinal use as prescribed or used by medical practitioners. Three other acts also control the use of drugs: the Customs and Excise Act, the Road Traffic Act and the Drug Trafficking Offences Act.

Under the MDA, controlled drugs fall into one of three categories according to their perceived danger and are also listed in five schedules which dictate how they should be stored, prescribed and documented. The three categories are Classes A, B or C.

Class A drugs
Class A are the drugs classified as the most dangerous, and penalties associated with them can be the most serious.

There are many Class A drugs but the ones parents reading this book are most likely to need to know about are cocaine, crack, heroin, opium, morphine, methadone, LSD and ecstasy. There are others, but they are drugs used in medicine and there is no record of them being used or misused by young people; examples are dipipanone (Diconal), pethidine, fentanyl and its derivatives. Any other drug prepared for injection, even if it falls into another category, is also deemed to be Class A.

Although magic mushrooms in themselves are not classified as a controlled drug and it is not illegal to eat them raw, the minute you do anything to them that is considered 'preparation' under the MDA, they become controlled. Once the mushroom's psychoactive component psilocybin or psilocin is 'prepared', i.e. crushed, cooked, dried or prepared in another way, it becomes a Class A drug.

Class B drugs
Class B drugs include amphetamine, cannabis, codeine and all 'misusable' barbiturates which can be prescribed. They are not illegal as such, although they are 'controlled', which means that if 'misused' their use can be deemed to be illegal. The barbiturates commonly misused are tuinal, nembutal, seconal, soneryl and amytal. Others in Class B are methaqualone, methylamphetamine, methylphenitade (Ritalin) and phenmet-razine. It is not unknown for young people to use some of these, although it is uncommon.

Class C drugs

These are the least severe in terms of the law, and include benzodiazepine tranquillisers like temazepam, dextropropoxyphene (Distalgesic, Doloxone) and other milder amphetamine stimulants. It is possible to be prosecuted for possession of temazepam, but not for other benzodiazepines.

Solvents are not classified as controlled drugs but it is an offence to sell them to anyone under eighteen if the retailer suspects that the substances will be misused.

The offences

Under the MDA, the act that most affects younger people caught in drugs offences, there are six categories of offence:
1. The unlawful possession of drugs
2. Possession with intent to supply
3. Unlawful supply
4. Unlawful production
5. Unlawful import or export
6. Permitting premises to be used for unlawful purposes.

The unlawful possession of drugs

This is the offence most commonly committed and is usually connected with cannabis. Younger people who commit an offence in this category are usually cautioned and do not get fines or custodial sentences. The vast majority of all drug offenders under twenty-five have offences connected to cannabis and are dealt with by being cautioned. Of the total number of people given immediate custody in 1995, the largest number received a sentence of one month or less. Of those fined, the majority received a fine between £20 and £100.

Most people who plead guilty to possession are cautioned. If the case goes to court, the defendant starts in the youth or magistrates' court and will usually be referred to crown court for a jury trial only if there is also a charge of supplying drugs. If the defendant pleads not guilty it is better if the case goes to crown court. This should always be discussed with a solicitor familiar with drugs cases. If someone is arrested in possession of drugs, the drugs are often sent away to be tested, which can take as long as three months. The defendant will be bailed and asked to return when the substance has been analysed. Then the person will be either cautioned or charged.

Unlawful possession is considered an offence under the MDA if someone knows they are in possession of the substance and the substance is found to be a controlled drug.

In order to be charged with unlawful possession, the prosecution must prove that the person knew of the existence of the controlled drug in their possession. If someone is caught with the substance in their hand there is no doubt. But if the substance is found in somewhere like a pocket or a car, and the person did not put it there or does not own it, whilst that in itself is considered a guilty act, it can argued that this does not prove guilty intent. In other words, it does not mean you knew or intended to do anything with it that would constitute an offence.

To some extent it's a matter of common sense. For example, if a lump of cannabis or a handful of pills or powders are found in someone's house whilst they are out, they are guilty of the act of possession. But if they can prove that someone else put them there, they are not guilty of intent. The law in this area is complicated and each case rests on its individual circumstances, which is why a solicitor should always be consulted.

Young people should be aware that if a group of them are found in possession of a cannabis joint which they are smoking in a park or on a street corner, for example, they can all be guilty of possession, whichever of them originally had possession of it. The same would apply to a group of people sharing a joint in their flat or anywhere else. If someone buys a substance offered to him or her as a drug and it turns out to be something else – for example, compressed tea or garden herbs instead of herbal marijuana, or aspirin instead of ecstasy – the person buying it could still be guilty of 'attempted possession'.

For parents it is important to note that if they remove drugs from their sons or daughters, they will not be deemed to be in possession of them if it is their intention to destroy them or pass them on to someone who can lawfully take possession of them. In the eyes of the law and within the bounds of common sense and probability, this would narrow a parent's option down to taking the drugs to the police. However, if they do that, they may well be involving their children in police investigation.

A further fine point of the law is that a parent's intention has to be that they are taking possession of the drug in order to prevent a criminal offence being committed: that is, taking cannabis to stop their children owning it. Saying you did it to stop them damaging their health is not a defence. Taking it away and destroying it or handing it to a police officer to stop someone else owning it, is a defence. However, destroying the drugs without dialogue with sons or daughters may not be the best thing to do in terms of your relationship with them. If parents are going to adopt the course of taking drugs to the police, they should certainly not do so before taking advice. If they do it on impulse because they are angry or frightened, they may well regret their actions both in terms of the legal consequences and their relationships with their children. Parents would be well advised to contact a drugs helpline such as Release, a local drugs agency or a solicitor, for advice as to who they should take the drugs to and what the consequences would be.

Unlawful supply and intent to supply

The law states that it is an offence to supply or intend to supply a controlled drug to another. The crucial point for parents to get across is that if the prosecution can prove that someone either passed or intended to pass controlled drugs to another person, this can be seen as an offence, even if there is no profit involved.

This is a more serious category of offence than possession on its own. But if a case comes to court, there are obviously evidential matters that affect the outcome. For example, someone caught with a small amount of a controlled drug, even if it is proved they intended to supply or supplied it to another, will face less serious consequences than someone caught with a larger amount of the drug and with what is known as drug paraphernalia. Paraphernalia would include scales, bags, cling film, knives, large amounts of money, mobile phones and drug lists – lists of phone numbers which might indicate people to whom the drugs are being supplied. The person charged with supply and intent to supply will often argue that the drugs were for their personal use only. It's obviously easier to prove that one cannabis plant, a small lump of cannabis or a small number of ecstasy tablets would be for one's own use, but large amounts arouse greater suspicion. Once again, this is a complex legal matter and if anyone is found with drugs and the police seek to bring a charge of supply or intent to supply, it is advisable to contact a solicitor immediately.

The number of people given immediate custodial sentences for unlawful supply and intent to supply in 1995 was 4,123, compared with less than half that number for possession. A total of 75,409 people were cautioned, fined or given non-custodial sentences for possession. Supply and intent to supply are serious offences and in the case of someone found to have supplied Class A drugs it would be unusual not to get a custodial sentence. In the case of Class B drugs, if the person proves they were not making a profit, has no previous convictions, was doing it on a small scale to friends only and the drug is cannabis, the person could get a fine, probation order or community service.

For parents who haven't managed to persuade their children to have no truck with drugs at all, the best advice to give them is not to carry drugs around or own them and only ever to have a small enough amount to show that it is for their consumption alone. If they are caught, they should know that the worst possible thing to do is try to swallow the whole lot. Any brush with the law is unpleasant and can be alarming, and being charged can have consequences for education and career. But it is not the end of the world, whereas swallowing handfuls of pills or lumps of cannabis could be very dangerous.

Unlawful production

The information here refers to cannabis, which is the only drug young people are likely to produce themselves. *Cannabis sativa* is not difficult to grow, either indoors or out. In some parts of the

world it grows wild. But it doesn't in the UK. Most police stations have pictures of all controlled drugs, and police officers know what they look like.

The proportion of people cautioned for cultivation has risen over the past decade from four per cent to thirty-six per cent, with a slight drop in 1995, the year in which it became a trafficking offence. It is now considered more serious than it was to produce cannabis unlawfully. The percentage of custodial sentences is not high, but anyone caught can expect at the least to be cautioned or fined.

It is not an offence to possess or supply cannabis seeds but anything done to germinate or grow them is an offence. If someone grows cannabis, they are committing both offences but can only be prosecuted for one of them. It is also an offence to let someone grow cannabis on your premises – an important point for parents.

The penalties for production depend on how many plants are grown and whether the person growing them was intending to supply the cannabis to other people. There is no separate charge for growing cannabis with the intent to supply, which means that the charge is the same whether someone is growing

one plant or a hundred or even several thousand. If the case goes to court, when it comes to passing sentence on the defendant, evidence will be put forward as to whether there was an intention to supply or not. There may be no direct evidence to support this either way, and then the prosecution will rely on how many plants are being cultivated, what kind of equipment is being used and what kind of harvest can be expected from the plants. If someone has a vast warehouse with hydroponic equipment to enhance the growth of several thousand plants, it is a different case from the teenager with one or two plants hidden in a corner of the house or garden.

A cannabis growing operation

Unlawful import or export

In practice, this does not affect many of the young drug users. But the illegal import and export of drugs can be serious offences and it's as well to know the rules.

Dependent users who are using heroin or methadone must obtain a special licence from the Home Office for what is called an 'open general licence' if they wish to travel abroad with a supply of heroin or methadone for their own use. The limit is 500 mg if the drug is in the form of an elixir (medicine) and 450 mg if in tablet form. The amounts are estimated to cover two weeks' average usage. If leaving the country for longer, and therefore needing to take more of the drug out, you have to apply for a 'licence for personal export'. The Home Office advises anyone seeking to do this to have a doctor's letter before applying. These licences only apply in the UK at the point of exit and entry and anyone travelling with them and with the limited amount of drugs is well advised to consult the British Embassy or consulate in the country they are going to, in order to establish what the laws are in that country in this regard.

It is the height of foolishness to go into another country or return to the UK carrying controlled drugs, even if for personal use only, unless licensed to do so.

When young people go abroad, they are occasionally tempted to carry something back into the UK for someone who tells them all they have to do is take a suitcase through and they will be financially rewarded. This has happened to several British people. The charity Prisoners Abroad (0171 833 3467), which helps British people in prison outside the UK, estimates that at any one time there are 1,000 young UK nationals in foreign prisons on drugs charges.

In some countries the laws against controlled drugs are very severe. It is never worth the risk of accepting any kind of mission to carry anything across a border, however much someone attempts to convince a person of the ease with which it can be done. In Thailand in 1991, a young teacher called Sandra Gregory who was short of cash and suffering from a tropical disease, agreed to smuggle drugs onto a Tokyo-bound flight for an acquaintance who she said had offered her £1,000. She was remanded for four years and in 1996 she found herself facing the death penalty. This was commuted to twenty-five years in jail. At the time of writing she has been transferred from Bangkok to London, where she will sit out the rest of her sentence. She wrote in *The Guardian*:

'The experience has made me ... appreciate what wonderful parents I have. They were my strength. They have been hounded by the press and suffered terribly since my arrest, but they never gave up on me.'

I heard recently of two young girls from Milton Keynes in their late teens, who were holidaying in Cyprus where a distant relative of one of them asked them to take some 'things' back to the UK for him. Luckily they were wary, refused the bribes and then found out that the 'things' were two suitcases containing heroin.

Permitting premises to be used for unlawful purposes

This applies mostly to clubs and other licensed premises. But it can apply to private premises as well. It is unlawful knowingly to occupy or manage premises where drugs are produced or supplied. To be proven guilty of this offence, the prosecution have to prove that the defendant knew what was going on. This is a strange law. For example, while it is illegal to allow opium or cannabis to be smoked, allowing cannabis to be cooked, cocaine to be snorted or heroin injected isn't an offence in this category. The MDA cites premises as being a house or a dance hall, but beyond that definition of premises is a muddle. In the case of parents, if your sons and daughters have a party while you are out, and controlled drugs are used, you would not necessarily be held responsible. If you were there, you could be.

Other offences

It is an offence knowingly to supply, or offer to supply, anything which can be used to take a controlled drug. You do not have to be selling it for this to be an offence. Needles and syringes are exempt.

Driving and drugs

Under the Road Traffic Act, it is an offence to be in charge of a motor vehicle on a road or other public place when unfit through drugs. If it is proved that someone is unfit through drugs while in charge, they can lose their licence for a year. If they have previous similar convictions, and there have been other factors such as an accident, or a car chase, the penalties can be more severe and can lead to a custodial sentence.

Police procedure

Stop and search

Drugs workers around the UK will tell you that the danger for most young people is being stopped and searched as they arrive at raves, clubs, festivals and similar events, or as they leave them. Of course parents will ask their children simply not to have drugs, and if they do, not to buy them from strangers, not to accept them from their friends and not to carry them. But once again, protest as they might that they would never have any truck with drugs, our children may not even be lying but simply intending never to have any truck and then finding themselves tempted. They need to know what happens if they are caught.

The laws regarding stop and search, arrest, treatment of people

held at police stations and certain elements of police investigation, are laid out under the Police and Criminal Evidence Act (PACE). The police can stop anyone on the street. If the person who is stopped can provide an explanation that satisfies the police there is nothing suspicious in their behaviour, then a search should be deemed unnecessary. The police can stop and search anyone without their permission if they have 'reasonable suspicion' that the person is carrying any of the following:

■ Controlled drugs, that is illegal drugs within the meaning of the Misuse of Drugs Act

■ An offensive weapon

■ A sharp object

■ Stolen goods.

They may also stop and search people on trains or coaches on their way to a sports stadium, or order stop and search in a given area when they suspect violence might occur. In this situation they do not need to have 'reasonable suspicion'.

Before stopping and searching anyone, the police must:

■ Produce a warrant card, if they are not in uniform

■ Give their name and the name of their police station

- Say exactly what their grounds for suspicion are

- Say exactly what they are looking for

- Tell people that they can get a copy of the search record if requested within one year.

The police can make a superficial search but are not allowed to do more than frisk and search pockets. If they decide a more intimate search is necessary, they must observe the rules, which are that an officer of the same sex should carry out the search, and that it should be done in a dignified manner.

Suggestions for parents

- It's worth trying to instil in young people that it is in their interests never to be alone in situations where they may come into contact with drugs, as well as knowing what can happen and what their rights are

- Try to make sure that they realise it is in their own interests that one member of their group stays straight and sober, and that if someone is stopped and searched by police or a bouncer outside a club, another bears witness to what is going on

- Encourage them to be fully aware of what trouble they can get into and how to deal with it

- Encourage them to know their rights if they are stopped and searched, or arrested for a drug related incident

- Encourage them not to challenge police officers because it definitely doesn't help their case

- Encourage them to remain polite but cautious in their conversations with police. They may unwittingly say things they may later regret. For example, saying their bit of cannabis is to share with a friend could be interpreted in law as supplying. It's best to keep communication to the politest minimum until they have seen a solicitor.

Release, the national drugs and legal service, have a 'Bust Card' which folds to pocket size like a driving licence and unfolds to give a condensed and very useful description of rights and advice on what to do if you are detained by the police. There are also telephone numbers of their twenty-four hour helplines. Parents could get cards from Release and give them to their sons and daughters. Send off for their publications list and also get a copy of *Drugs and The Law*, £1.75 p and p, available from Release, 388 Old Street, London EC1V 9LT.

The police caution

The caution is used as an alternative to charging someone. The person being cautioned must admit their guilt and the caution must be dealt with by a police officer of the rank of inspector or above. The caution does not constitute a criminal record and is wiped off the computer after five years.

In order to issue a caution, police must have sufficient evidence of the offender's guilt to give them a realistic chance of conviction. Either the person being cautioned, or a parent or guardian of someone under seventeen, must understand the significance of a caution and give informed consent to being cautioned.

In 1980 only one per cent of all those dealt with by the criminal justice system for drug offences were cautioned. In 1995, over fifty-two per cent were cautioned. In the past, a far greater proportion went to jail and paid fines.

Police forces differ from one area of the UK to another in their drugs policies and their views about what the prevailing attitude should be to those who break the law for reasons to do with drugs. But there is consensus that the harm reduction path is the most sensible one to follow. In 1994 the Home Office body, the Advisory Council on the Misuse of Drugs, wrote that the elimination of drug misuse is 'generally regarded as an unobtainable goal'. It says that containment rather than elimination of drug misuse is a 'realistic objective'. The Council recommends that 'Enforcement should support the efforts of other agencies working to reduce the harm caused by drug misuse'.

You can find out what local policy is by contacting the local police or drugs agency or law centre. Some forces go for 'zero tolerance' and do not favour the use of cautions, others take an enlightened and more liberal approach. Young people who may be vulnerable to being stopped and searched and perhaps charged with possession, the most common charge, need to know what to expect. In some areas there are schemes in which police refer young people they catch committing drug offences to the local drugs advice and treatment agency. Some young people will be so relieved to get off with a caution that they may fall into a fool's paradise. Cautions may not constitute custodial sentences, fines or even community service orders, but they are serious and remain on record for five years.

Police in England and Wales may use cautions instead of initiating prosecution through the courts. This procedure doesn't exist in Scotland where it is up to the local procurator fiscal to decide whether to prosecute or not. The Scottish equivalent to a caution would be a warning from the procurator fiscal.

What happens if someone is detained?

If someone is detained, they have the right to be treated humanely and with respect. They should be dealt with 'expeditiously and released as soon as the need for detention has ceased to apply'. They have the right of access to written rules about their rights in detention and the right to speak to the custody officer in charge of them. A custody record of everything that happens whilst in detention must be kept. Most people aren't kept for more than a few hours before being released or charged. In serious cases the maximum a person can be held for is thirty-six hours without being charged or released.

Anyone detained at a police station has the right to legal representation. There are two ways to deal with this. Parents can anticipate the chance of their sons and daughters being picked up and give them the name and telephone number of a solicitor of their choice, or failing that, once detained the young person can insist on seeing the duty solicitor. There is always one available and this service is provided free of charge. Anyone detained is well advised to say as little as possible until the solicitor arrives to advise them. Anyone detained has the right to one telephone call, although not the right to make the call themselves.

Being detained can be alarming, especially for a young person unfamiliar with the inside of a police station, let alone a cell. It is best to try to keep as cool and calm as possible. PC Alan Finch, a Community Involvement Officer in Molesey police station in Kingston-upon-Thames, says:

'Young people know that using drugs is wrong, so when they're

caught there is an element of cockiness in their attitude. It's something of a shock to find that Mr Nice from talks at school has become Mr Nasty who "cuffs and searches". ["Cuffs" are handcuffs.] On the street the stop and search is only a cursory search of outer clothing, but if there is a likelihood of something being concealed, the officer will do the search at the police station. A "normal" young person will be treated as a potential criminal. But there has to be justification for stopping and searching someone. This is either because the officer believes that the young person is likely to hurt themselves or is showing signs of intoxication or is aggressive in manner, or the officer fears for his or her safety. This means in effect, they may be handcuffed whilst being searched.

'Many police stations have caged walkways to the custody suite. Walking along it can be quite frightening. After being booked in, which at a busy time will mean sitting among drunks, domestic fights and generally rather frightening scenes, they will be searched again if drugs are suspected; this will be by an officer of the same sex. A strip search will occur very rarely and be observed by an appropriate adult.'

An 'appropriate adult' is anyone a young person under seventeen chooses to have there with them: it might be a parent, guardian, friend or social worker – whoever the young person chooses. If the young person doesn't want the appropriate adult there, they have the right to request this. A strip search can take place anywhere that is considered private, and the usual procedure is for one item of clothing to be removed at a time. For example you take off your shirt and keep on your trousers or skirt, replace the top and remove the trousers or skirt. Police are only allowed to do this if the custody officer 'reasonably considers' it is necessary to remove something a person should not be keeping.

If they then suspect that something is hidden internally in someone's body, the police must get permission for an intimate body search in writing from an officer of at least the rank of superintendent. This person then has to have 'reasonable grounds' for believing that a Class A drug cannot be found without such a search. The search must be carried out by a registered medical practitioner or nurse in a doctor's surgery, hospital or other place used for medical purposes. Such intimate body searches are very rare among young people. However, police do have the right to take non-intimate body samples including hair (not pubic), samples from under the nails, a swab from any part of the body including the mouth but excluding other orifices, saliva and foot prints or impressions of the body apart from the hand.

Police can request a blood or urine sample – these too come under the intimate search rules – and a person can refuse. But refusal will be used by the prosecution to suggest guilt, should the case go to court. Cannabis can stay in blood and urine for up to thirty days or even longer for habitual users, but in someone who only uses it occasionally, it won't show up for more than about one week. Other drugs usually remain present for about twenty-four hours. In reality it is extremely unusual for anyone to be blood or urine tested. Results cannot be used to prove possession but can be used in a case of someone who is caught driving whilst unfit through drugs.

PC Alan Finch continues his description of what a young person can expect at a police station:

'Once they have arrived and gone through what I have already described, they will then be locked in either a cell or a detention room if one is available until an appropriate adult arrives. In the cell they will be on their own. There is a hatch in the door through which they will be observed every half hour, even while on the lavatory. There is a feeling of being trapped in a box. The arresting officer who knew about the person may have gone. The jailer may have no personal knowledge of the young person. Outside on a busy day or night the noise can be alarming: shouts, screams, crashes, bangs, and if the alarm bell in the cell is rung, it may take the officer some time to get there. It is a case of sitting it out until the appropriate adult arrives. This can take as long as eight hours so it can be traumatic. It is a hostile environment with a limited amount of caring.

'A full explanation will be given to the adult when they arrive and there may be an interview which will be taped. Parents may show an extreme reaction of anger and crying. Any substance found on the young person may be sent off to be analysed to establish what it is. Throughout the country what happens next can differ. Some would require a full report and a consultation with other agencies, others will formally charge a person straight away with no option but to send them to court. Or they might be cautioned. But for this to happen, they will have to be unlikely to re-offend, show remorse and to admit to the offence. The evidence will have to be looked at, as well as any previous cautions. Seven out of ten youngsters cautioned do not re-offend. In this area at the moment we are heading in the direction of zero tolerance. In effect this means a caution is unlikely and the young person will be sent to court regardless of the circumstances.'

Sergeant Mark Fraser who also works at the Youth and Community Section of Molesey police station, adds:

'If you talk to young people like adults they respect you. Young people aren't stupid and if you try to lord it over them they will have no respect for you and you'll lose your credibility. We have to put young people under seventeen in detention rooms while waiting for the parents in order to protect them from some of the more violent elements that may be in the station. When the parents arrive the child is interviewed, with the solicitor present if one has been requested. There are some parents who want their child to go to court and if the young person is denying the offence, we can't caution them and have to put them through the courts. We look at each case on its merits and if it's appropriate we do give a caution.

'Parents are usually very shocked but I've never seen a parent hit a child in the station. They are astounded, they are embarrassed to be in a police station, they feel betrayed that their children have breached their trust. They feel shame and so do the young people. They feel they have let their parents down and they too feel ashamed about having caused their parents to be in the police station. It's this feeling of shame that they remember more than the police station itself and it usually stops them doing anything again.'

Is there a right to silence?

There is a lot of confusion about this. There used to be a right to silence, and there still is, but the consequences of using it have changed. *Drugs and the Law*, the excellent pamphlet by Release, explains the issue clearly:

'The Criminal Justice Act 1994 amended the right to silence, it did not remove it. A person detained at a police station does not have to answer questions or give explanations as to their behaviour. However, if they refuse to answer questions at the appropriate time and are later charged with a crime or they give an explanation which they later contradict at the trial this can, in certain situations, be taken into account by the court in deciding whether they are guilty or innocent. Many defendants are convicted of offences because of verbal admissions made to the police. Such admissions become part of the evidence against the defendant at their subsequent trial. The police are trained in interrogation and are aware that some drug users in custody can be disorientated and confused and this can be exploited. Some people are prepared to do anything or say anything to get out of the police station, even make false admissions as to guilt.'

At the point when the police arrest someone, they will say: 'You do not have to say anything … But it may harm your defence if you do not mention when questioned, something which you later rely on in court. Anything you do say may be given in evidence.'

The interview

Interviews are conducted at the police station and the proceedings are tape recorded. A solicitor should be present unless the young person for some reason has turned down the option of having one there. It is always best to have someone to represent and advise anyone detained in a police station. What is said by the young person during this interview is crucial and could be used against them subsequently. The interview is a purely fact-finding exercise and not one in which you need to prove your innocence. At the end the police have a number of options:

■ They can keep the person in custody while they carry out further enquiries; this is usually a maximum of twenty-four hours although it can be extended to thirty-six hours in special circumstances

■ They can release the person without charge because they have insufficient evidence to charge someone or are satisfied of their innocence

■ They can release the person on police bail, with the instruction to return at a given time

■ They can give a caution if the person detained has admitted to the offence, they don't consider it serious enough to prosecute through the courts, and they are satisfied that they can prove their case.

Sentences

The more severe penalties can only be imposed at the Crown Courts before a judge and jury. Magistrates cannot impose more than a six month sentence or a £5,000 fine. Obviously every case depends on individual circumstances and maximum fines and sentences do not automatically apply.

	Possession	Supply
Class A	7 years + fine	Life + fine
Class B	5 years + fine	14 years + fine
Class C	2 years + fine	5 years + fine

Definition of Penalties

There are four penalties which may be imposed:

■ Immediate custody – this means offenders are sent straight to prison when found guilty through the courts

■ Probation – if someone is put on probation, this means they have to report to a probation officer at fixed times for a fixed period. It is rare for this period to extend beyond two years. There may be conditions attached; for example, a drug offender may have to attend a rehab

■ Community service order – the offender has to fulfil a set number of hours working for free in the community. This could involve anything from painting and decorating, working for a charity, cleaning the streets and so on. It is possible that a drug offender would be asked to work in a drugs agency or work as a volunteer in such a place

■ Combination order – this combines probation and community service.

Young offenders

Up until the age of seventeen, people are dealt with as young offenders, in the young offenders' courts. The maximum sentence that can be imposed in young offenders' courts is one year in a young offenders' institution. After they turn eighteen they are treated as adults and go through the magistrates' courts which can impose a maximum sentence of two years. If the offence is seen to warrant it, the offender can be referred to the crown courts but until they are twenty-one, any sentence is served in a young offenders' institution.

The ones who go to jail

Thirty-five per cent of all drug offences are committed by people under twenty-one. That looks alarming. It looks like a huge number of our sons and daughters, and it is: some 32,770 young people. But eighty-two per cent of all drug offences are related to cannabis. Of these almost ninety per cent are for possession, the least serious of all drug related crime, the category of use that means you have the drug only for yourself and do not intend either to share it with anyone or sell it to anyone.

Those 32,770 have not all gone to jail. In fact only a very small minority have: 908 in 1995, 857 young men and 51 young women. Nobody has done any research into who these 908 are or what their offences were. The fact that there is no research into these young people who are receiving custodial sentences is something that parents of such young people might like to take up with their local MPs.

Research is very important in any analysis of what can be done to reduce the harm caused to young people themselves and their families and friends, and the knock-on effects on the rest of us, by heavy-end drug crime. Most of the government money spent on tackling drug misuse goes on enforcement. Neither treatment nor research gets enough funding. We hear a lot about young people and their use of drugs, we hear more about any aspect of drug use that causes damage, despair or danger, particularly when young people are involved. How come there is no analysis of these 908 people under the age of twenty-one who get custodial sentences? Surely it makes sense to work out why they are caught up in drug offences serious enough to incur a criminal record?

Anyone needing a full list of the classes of controlled drugs and any detail on the law regarding drugs could contact Release or look at a copy of *Misuse of Drugs and Trafficking Offences,* by Rudi Fortson, published by Sweet and Maxwell. This book costs £42, but should be available in a good reference library.

Drugs glossary

Alcohol

Alcoholic drinks chiefly consist of water and ethyl alcohol (or ethanol), produced by the fermentation of fruits, vegetables or grains. How much effect a drink has depends on its strength and how quickly it is drunk, whether consumers have any food in their stomachs, the body weight, personality and surroundings of the drinker. Since tolerance develops, the effects will also depend on how much the person is used to drinking.

As far as long-term use is concerned, effects are related to the amount a person drinks. The worst forms of physical damage are only commonly seen after substantial tolerance has developed and the individual has become heavily dependent ('alcoholic'). Heavy drinking encourages obesity and stomach and liver disorders and can result in brain damage. Heavy drinking by pregnant women (six units or more a day) can result in fetal abnormality and babies with withdrawal symptoms and developmental problems. Cases of this 'fetal alcohol syndrome' are rare in Britain. If alcohol is taken at the same time as other depressant drugs, the effects of both on the nervous system is exaggerated, with a consequent increase in the dangers of intoxication and overdose. Since alcohol use is so much part of many people's everyday life, it is one of the drugs most likely to be taken at the same time as another.

The manufacture, sale, purchase and distribution of alcoholic drinks are controlled by licensing regulations. There are no laws against possessing or drinking alcohol, except that under the Public Order Act 1986 it is an offence to carry or possess alcohol on trains, coaches or minibuses travelling to and from designated sports events. Some cities have introduced by-laws prohibiting public consumption in city centre areas. Licensing laws also restrict opening times, although the laws have become more relaxed. There are regional variations and hours are more restricted on Sunday. In relation to age, the law says: it is an offence to give alcohol to a child under five. There are strict regulations regarding times and parts of pubs into which children can go. At fourteen children can enter the bar of licensed premises, but can't have alcohol until they're eighteen, when they can legally buy alcohol. Sixteen year-olds can buy beer, cider or perry (and in Scotland wine), but only to drink with a meal not served at a bar. It is an offence to be drunk in a public place – including licensed premises – to be drunk and disorderly, or to drive while unfit to do so because of drink. It is also an offence to drive with more than 80 mg of alcohol in every 100 ml of blood. Unlicensed 'home-brewing' of beers, wines and cider (not spirits) is permitted, but the products cannot be sold.

Over ninety per cent of the adult population drink to a greater or lesser extent. On average men drinkers consume the equivalent of 1.5 pints of beer a day, women about 0.5 pint. One in five men drink 3.5 to 4 pints or more at least once a week. Despite the licensing laws, around sixty per cent of children aged between thirteen and seventeen are likely to have bought alcohol in a pub or off-license. In the thirteen to sixteen age range, about a third of children drink at least once a week, but mostly in the home and generally small amounts.

Alkyl nitrites
(poppers; brand names include KIX, Rock Hard, TNT, Rush)

There are various types of poppers which are collectively known as alkyl nitrites. They are clear, yellow, volatile and flammable liquids; in effect, they are solvents. The two most common are amyl nitrite and butyl nitrite. Amyl nitrite's main medical use is as an antidote to cyanide poisoning.

Street nitrites usually come in stoppered glass bottles about the size of Tipp-ex. They are inhaled straight from the bottle or from a cloth. The effects are almost instantaneous and last for two to five minutes. There is a 'rush' as the blood vessels dilate, heart-beat quickens and the blood rushes to the brain. Consequently, pounding headache, dizziness, a flushed face and neck and 'light-headedness' are commonly reported. Those using the drug to enhance sexual pleasure claim prolonged sensation of orgasm and prevention of premature ejaculation, although some have reported problems with achieving erection.

The only alkyl nitrite under any sort of legislation is amyl nitrite which is classified as a pharmacy medicine. The most common of the nitrites is butyl nitrite. The nitrites are primarily associated with the male gay community although recent surveys suggest that the drug is becoming more common among the wider population, including younger teenagers. Available in sex shops, clubs and bars etc., costing up to £5 a bottle.

Amphetamines
(speed, uppers, co-pilots, jelly beans, whizz)

They are synthetic stimulants, drugs which act on the central nervous system to increase neural activity in the brain. Most of the illegal amphetamine used by young people is in the form of amphetamine sulphate.

Amphetamine sulphate is usually sold in the form of white crystalline powder and is smoked, snorted, dissolved in a drink, dabbed on the tongue or rubbed into the gums which tingle; the intensity of tingling is supposed to indicate the strength of the drug. Amphetamine also comes in tablet form. Some people inject it.

Amphetamine arouses and activates the user much as the body's natural adrenaline does in the face of emergencies or stress. Breathing and heart-rate speed up, the pupils widen and appetite lessens. The user can feel more alert, energetic, confident and cheerful and less bored or tired. Higher doses can cause intense exhilaration, rapid flow of ideas and feelings of greatly increased physical and mental capacity. The effects of a single dose last about three to four hours and leave the user feeling tired: it can take the body a couple of days to recover, even after small doses. Some people feel depressed for a few days after taking amphetamines. This is because the energy increase caused by amphetamine is not 'extra' and does not come free: it's borrowed and has to be paid back. A few people become psychologically dependent on amphetamines and in a very few cases amphetamine psychosis can develop (see page 91). But this generally goes once the drugs is no longer used.

All amphetamines are prescription only drugs under the Medicines Act and with the exception of adfax and ponderax they are also controlled under the Misuse of Drugs Act. The ones which are used by the drug-taking public are amphetamine, dex- and methyl-amphetamine, phenmet-razine and methylphenidate and are in class B of the Act, but if these are prepared for injection, the increased penalties of class A apply. Milder amphetamine-related stimulants like diethylpropion appear in class C.

Amphetamine retails at around £10-£15 a gram. Most recreational users buy £5 'wraps', so called because the powder is wrapped in something or bits of paper.

Amphetamine base
(base)

This is a grey-coloured, putty-like substance which is made during the manufacturing process before amphetamine becomes a powder. It can be anything up to seventy per cent pure. It is smoked, injected or wrapped up in cigarette paper and swallowed. See amphetamine. In addition it is reportedly highly caustic and will burn veins, nose or stomach depending on how it is ingested. It is a Class B drug unless it is prepared for injection. Base is more expensive than amphetamine powder by weight (£20-£25 a gram) but is much stronger. Its prevalence in the UK is not known at the time of writing, although anecdotally it is not unknown and drugs workers around the UK hear about it.

Methylamphetamine
(ice, meth, crystal, glass)

This is a highly potent amphetamine. A new smokable form of methylamphetamine known as 'ice' is reported to be available in the UK. It is produced from methylamphetamine hydrochloride by a conversion process into clear, glassy, rock-like crystals, hence the slang names. Colourless, tasteless and odourless, it can be between ninety and a hundred per cent pure. 'Ice' is rarely seen in the UK but it has been known to be used at some British dance venues. Effects are much the same as amphetamines and last between two to sixteen hours. It is chemically related to amphetamine sulphate but is significantly more active. It is a Class B drug.

Amyl nitrite
See Alkyl nitrites.

Anabolic steroids
They are one group of hormones (e.g. testosterone) which occur naturally in the body and are responsible for the development of the reproductive organs. Testosterone is also responsible for masculine characteristics such as the growth of body hair and deep voice. They are often used to build up muscle tissue. Most of the synthetic anabolic steroids on the market are derived from testosterone.

They can be swallowed as a pill or capsule and also injected. As used by athletes and bodybuilders, these drugs are taken in multiple combinations over cycles of six to eight weeks in dosages far in excess of therapeutic recommendations.

Users often report that they make them feel more aggressive and they can train harder and recover more quickly from strenuous exercise. Over time, women users may become more 'masculine' and it may well be that the effects are irreversible. These characteristics may be passed on to a female fetus if the woman is pregnant while taking the drugs. In men, the reproductive system may become temporarily affected. Other long-term effects include liver and kidney disorders and reduced sperm count; some men may also show over-development of breasts which may not be reversible. Steroids can affect growth in young people who haven't yet reached full height.

Anabolic steroids are prescription only drugs. They are also controlled under Class C of the Misuse of Drugs Act whereby it is illegal to supply the drugs, but not illegal to possess them for personal use.

There are few statistics available on the illicit use of steroids. What is known is that their use is common among those devoted to building muscular strength and has recently been seen among young people who want to look good without becoming over-muscled. The street cost on average is around £20 for 100 tablets.

Barbiturates
(barbs, downers, sleepers)

They are what are known as hypnosedatives, i.e. drugs which calm people down (sedatives) and in higher doses act as sleeping pills (hypnotics).

They come as tablets or capsules in various sizes and colours. They are not popular with the teenaged recreational drug user but are used by some heavy-end dependent drug users who dissolve barbiturates in water and inject them into their veins. While all barbiturates depress the central nervous system, they vary in effect, duration, and toxicity. They provide temporary relief from fears, tension and anxiety. The user can appear to be drunk. The effects are considerably increased when combined with alcohol and other drugs and can last up to sixteen hours.

Sudden withdrawal from very high doses of barbiturates can be fatal. Assuming there are no serious complications, withdrawal effects subside within about a week. Heavy users are vulnerable to bronchitis and pneumonia (because the cough reflex is depressed), hypothermia (because peripheral blood vessels dilate, but the drug blocks normal responses to cold) and repeated accidental overdose (due to mental confusion and tolerance effects, heavy users often take excessive doses). Most of these hazards are increased if the drug is taken by injection, when infection and a build-up of undissolved tablet in the skin tissue may occur.

They are Class B drugs. Because of the widespread availability of benzodiazepines, the tighter controls on barbiturates and the rise in heroin use, barbiturates are a negligible part of the illicit drug scene. However, opiate users unable to obtain their usual supply of heroin sometimes take them to ward off withdrawal symptoms.

Benzodiazepines
(benzos, jellies, goosies, temazzies)

These are the most commonly prescribed tranquillisers and hypnotics. As tranquillisers they produce the relief of anxiety, and sedation. As hypnotics, they aid sleep. They include valium, librium, nobrium, mogadon, ativan, normison (temazepam), dalmane and rohypnol.

Benzodiazepines are taken as tablets or capsules. Temazepam, one of the best known and one used by people with a heroin dependency to aid sleep and relaxation, comes as a gel in a capsule and is injected by heroin dependent users. Benzodiazepines depress mental activity and alertness and relieve tension and anxiety. Some people feel drowsy, lethargic and forgetful after first taking them. The effects can last four to eight hours. High doses of benzodiazepines can cause overdose, especially if mixed with opiate drugs like heroin or methadone, or alcohol. If taken by pregnant women, there is a risk that the baby will have withdrawal symptoms.

They are Class C drugs which makes supplying them without a prescription illegal. But it is not illegal to possess them in medicinal form without a prescription, with the exception of temazepam.

They are the most commonly prescribed drugs in Britain, with about one in seven British adults taking them at some point. It is believed that up to half of the prescriptions issued are done so without the doctor seeing the patient. However there has been a fall in prescriptions since 1979, from just over 30 million to just over 14 million in 1994. During the mid-1980s, non-medicinal use of temazepam became a serious concern in some areas of Scotland, where at the time, heroin supply had been significantly reduced and users were looking for a more easily injectable substitute.

In 1989, the manufacturers changed the formulation of temazepam from a liquid to a gel to discourage users from injecting the drug, but the practice continued as users dissolved the gel for injecting by heating it. Doctors have now been banned from prescribing any formulation of temazepam other than hard tablets. They are also used by some regular clubbers who sometimes take them to help them come down and sleep after taking amphetamine, LSD, ecstasy or cocaine.

Rohypnol, a diamond shaped purple tablet, has achieved some notoriety in the United States as the 'date rape drug', said to have been given to young women unwittingly who cannot subsequently recall exactly what happened to them whilst they were under its influence. It has not made an impact on the UK scene but reports from Scotland suggest it might be replacing temazepam as the street tranquilliser most popular with users because it is not illegal to possess it without a prescription. As well as being the drug of choice for many injectors, tranquillisers are used by opiate users either when their drug of choice is in short supply or they cannot afford it; to augment the effects of other depressant drugs like alcohol and heroin or to offset the stimulant effects of amphetamine and ecstasy.

Single tablets on the street fetch up to £4.

Butyl nitrite
See Alkyl nitrites.

Caffeine
Caffeine is a nervous system stimulant found in coffee, tea and soft drinks, and in over-the-counter analgesics and headache pills. One strong cup of 'real' coffee may contain caffeine equivalent to the minimal stimulant dose. A cup of tea generally contains less, but can contain almost as much caffeine as instant coffee. Soft drinks also generally contain less caffeine than coffee, but because of their lower body weight, children consuming a full can of drinks containing caffeine could ingest the equivalent of four cups of coffee.

In moderate doses (150 to 250 mg) the drug allays drowsiness and fatigue and postpones the onset of sleep, helping prevent boredom and tiredness interfering with manual and intellectual tasks. Larger doses impair performance, especially where delicate co-ordination of movement is required. Physiological effects can include increased heart rate, raised blood pressure, increased excretion of urine (these diminish with repeated use), constriction of blood vessels in the brain (relieving some types of headache) and increased breathing. Coffee, even when it is decaffeinated, increases stomach acidity. Effects of coffee are evident within an hour, lasting three to four hours. Afterwards there can be a let-down effect of increased fatigue.

People consuming the caffeine equivalent of seven or more cups of strong coffee a day may feel anxious and irritable, and experience muscle tremor and headache. The stimulant effect may also cause insomnia, but such disturbances clear up once caffeine intake is reduced. Dependence, mainly psychological, can develop to the extent that people find it hard to stop drinking coffee, even for medical reasons.

Caffeine is not subject to any legal prohibitions on its manufacture, sale, distribution or possession.

Seventy per cent of all UK adults drink coffee and eighty-six per cent drink tea.

Cannabis
(puff, dope, ganja, hash, pot, shit, draw, blow)

Cannabis is derived from a bushy plant called *Cannabis sativa*. It is consumed in one of three forms: herbal cannabis (everything except seeds and stalks), cannabis resin (dark brown or green) and cannabis oil. There are many varieties of cannabis, some more potent than others. Two of the best known and most potent kinds of the herbal cannabis are skunk and sinsemilla. Sinsemilla is made of the more powerful female flower heads before they are pollinated. Skunk is intensively grown in special circumstances to increase its strength. The onset of the effects are often quicker than with ordinary cannabis and users have reported elation, profound relaxation, alteration of time and perception, transient hallucinations (although not in the same league as LSD), increased sociability, anxiety, mild paranoia, and the 'munchies'. It is popular because skunk buds are difficult to fake, whereas resin has been adulterated with everything from boot polish to ketamine. The street names for cannabis change regularly.

The resin is scraped or rubbed from the plant, and then compressed into blocks. Cannabis is usually smoked, either in a cigarette or pipe, with (resin) or without (herbal) tobacco. The resin is crumbled up into tobacco and made into a roll-up. Home-made devices called 'bongs' are also used: they are water pipes which cool down the smoke. Cannabis can also be cooked in food or eaten straight.

As with many drugs, the mood of a person can determine the effects experienced. Normally it assists relaxation and heightens the senses. It can also make people more talkative and open. It very often increases hunger (the 'munchies'). There is still no conclusive evidence, and the controversies continue over whether long-term cannabis use causes lasting damage to physical or mental health.

Cannabis is a Class B drug. It is by far the most commonly used drug in this country, with an estimated 8 million people having tried it at least once. Nearly a quarter of those surveyed in the sixteen to twenty-nine age range had tried cannabis. Many young people travel to Holland to use the 'coffee shops' which legally sell many varieties of cannabis, often growing their own. Its most common form in this country is resin, with the herbal cannabis also popular. Oil is rare.

Cannabis in herbal form is sold for £100 to £150 an ounce. Most users would buy a quarter or an eighth, for which they pay about £25 to £40 or £13 to £20 respectively. Resin is about £100 an ounce.

2CB
(nexus, spectrum, bromo)

Its full name is 4-bromo-2,5,-dimethoxyphenethylamine. It is related to ecstasy and has been seen in the form of a red pill or white powder. In the UK it has so far been found in drug seizures as a mixed formulation with MBDB (see below), in the form of a white tablet with a dollar or pound sign motif. Effects include heightened visual imagery, body awareness and tactile sensitivity, lasting for about six hours. Some people take it with ecstasy to heighten the effect. It is a Class A drug. It is difficult to say who is using it or how popular it is, but the ISDD believes the main consumers are ecstasy users.

Cocaine
(coke, charlie, snow)

Cocaine is extracted from the coca shrub found in the Andean region of South America. As an illicit drug it is usually used as a white powder scraped into 'lines' with a razor blade and snorted up the nose through a rolled-up bank note. It can also be injected or smoked. It is a stimulant and has similar effects to amphetamines. It can produce feelings of well-being, great physical strength and mental capacity. Hunger can disappear and the user can become oblivious to pain and fatigue. The effects last for about two hours.

Repeated sniffing damages the membranes lining the nose and may also damage the structure separating the nostrils. Repeated smoking may cause respiratory problems such as cracked, wheezy breathing and also partial loss of voice. It is not physically addictive, but psychological dependence can build up and in rare cases, people develop what is known as cocaine psychosis which usually disappears within a few weeks of the drug not being taken. Pregnant women are advised not to use cocaine as it can cause medical complications such as placental separation and bleeding.

Cocaine is a Class A drug. Despite being expensive at around £60 to £100 a gram, and considered a rich man's drug, its use is not confined to those with plenty of money. There are approximately ten lines to a gram. Many polydrug users (those who use many drugs) take it on an occasional 'treat' basis.

Crack
(rock, freebase, wash, stone)

Crack is a much stronger form of cocaine which consists of small clusters of cocaine crystals known as rock or crack. It is called crack because it makes a crackling noise as it burns. How much a rock costs depends on locality and supply but it averages at around £10 to £20 for a rock about the size of a raisin. Crack is smoked on tin foil in a pipe or glass tube. The rocks are heated until they evaporate and the smoke is inhaled.

The 'hit' is much greater than cocaine but lasts for no more than ten minutes and can produce intense cravings for more. As with cocaine, if expectant mothers use crack there is a danger of spontaneous abortions, separation of the placenta and stillbirth.

It is a Class A drug. Crack was found in two-fifths of all cocaine seizures in 1995, approximately 1,460 seizures. Its street use is prevalent in small pockets of many UK cities.

Drug misuse databases

The old addict register on which dependent users were listed by name was ended in 1997. The regional databases in England, Scotland and Wales continue to collect the numbers of drug users coming forward for treatment. Names and personal details are not now entered on the database. There is no legal requirement for notification of data to the databases, but it is in the health professionals' interests to do so for funding purposes and to build up a picture of how many drug users are coming forward for treatment.

Drug detection periods

This is a brief, rough guide to how long different drugs can be detected in urine after use at dose levels typically taken by drug misusers.

Amphetamine	2 – 4 days
Cannabis	casual use 2 –7 days; heavy use up to 30 days
Ecstasy	2 – 4 days
Diazepam	1 – 2 days
Temazepam	1 – 2 days
Alcohol	12 – 24 hours
Heroin	1 – 2 days
Buprenorphine	2 – 3 days
Cocaine	12 hours – 3 days
Methadone	2 days
LSD	2 – 3 days

GHB
(GBH)

This drug's full name is gammahydroxybutyrate or sodium oxybate. It was developed in the United States as an anaesthetic used as a premedication to promote sleep before surgery, and has sedative rather than painkilling effects. It is a colourless, odourless liquid with a slightly salty taste which is sold in small bottles. Because of the way it is made, there is no telling how concentrated the liquid is. A bottle could contain around three grams of the drug, in theory quite a mild dose, or up to 20 grams, a very high dose. It is consumed orally in liquid form.

The effects are noticeable between ten minutes and an hour after taking the drug and have been reported as lasting a day or longer. It has been described as 'liquid ecstasy'. As the dosage is increased, euphoria gives way to powerful sedative effects and it has been known to cause nausea, vomiting, disorientation, convulsions, coma and respiratory collapse. There have been no confirmed deaths from taking GHB.

It is classed as a medicine, so possession is not an offence. However, unauthorised manufacture and distribution could be an offence under the Medicines Act.

At the moment, it is difficult to gauge numbers using the drug, but there are two types of people using it. Bodybuilders use it because it promotes what is known as 'slow wave sleep', during which growth hormone is secreted. Another group of users are those on the dance and club scene. Its use has particularly been noted in gay clubs. Prices have been reported at around £5 for a capful of liquid and £10 to £15 a bottle.

Herbal ecstasy
(one brand name is Cloud 9)

Herbal ecstasy is a legal product and contains a number of herbs from around the world. It is presently sold in capsule form through mail order. All of the herbs in herbal ecstasy are mild stimulants, although some have uses in herbal medicine. There is some dispute concerning its effects, with reports ranging from its being similar to ecstasy, to being no more than a caffeine-type high. Its health risks are as yet unknown and its use is at present rare in this country, it being more prominent in the Californian rave scene. One firm sells it at £65 for ten capsules.

Heroin
See opiates

Ketamine
(K, Special K)

This is an anaesthetic with analgesic and psychedelic properties chemically related to PCP. It is taken either in its liquid pharmaceutical form for injecting or as pills or powders that can be snorted or smoked. Users say that under its influence they assume a different point of view, outside of body and self. It takes effect over varying time periods depending on the route of administration – from thirty seconds for intravenous injection to twenty minutes when taken orally – and the effects can last up to three hours. Reported physical effects include an initial cocaine-like 'rush', vomiting and nausea, slurred speech, blurred vision, numbness and ataxia (irregular muscle co-ordination). There is little literature on the consequences of long-term use.

Ketamine is not controlled under the Misuse of Drugs Act, and possession is not an offence. However, unauthorised supply is illegal as it is a prescription only medicine (although the maximum penalties are relatively mild).

Ketamine appears on the dance scene but is rare. Prices range from £6 to £25 for a wrap of powder, though this may not always be ketamine.

Khat
(qat, chat)

Khat is a leafy plant cultivated throughout eastern Africa and the Arabian peninsula. It is chewed or drunk as tea. The active ingredients start to deteriorate two days after the plant has been harvested, so it must be consumed fresh. It is predominantly stimulant in effect. A typical chewing session is said to be the equivalent of ingesting a moderate 5 mg dose of amphetamine sulphate. Following mild euphoria and talkativeness, users have often reported calming effects. Khat affects the oral cavity and the digestive tract. Inflammation of the mouth and other parts of the oral cavity with secondary infections is common in khat users. There also appears to be the risk of oral cancer.

The active ingredients are Class C drugs. However, the fact that these drugs are controlled does not mean that khat leaves are illegal. The courts may consider them illegal if they have in some way been prepared or formed into a product. There is little evidence to suggest that khat is being used in the UK except in Somalian, Ethiopian and Arabian peninsula communities.

LSD
(acid, tabs, trips)

Its full name is lysergic acid diethylamide and it is a powerful hallucinogen.

Although LSD is a white powder, it is very rare for it to be taken in this form. Normally LSD in liquid form has been dropped onto blotting paper, gelatine or sugar cubes which are swallowed or dissolved under the tongue. The blotting paper often carries designs or images from popular culture (e.g. Batman, Sonic the Hedgehog etc.).

The effects last between eight and twelve hours. A person's senses change and time can seem to change or even disappear. Everything takes on a new perspective. The type of 'trip' experienced often depends on the mood of the person just prior to consumption. There are dangers from the illusions and delusions that can be created by LSD where people think they can accomplish the impossible, but deaths related to this are very rare. There is also evidence to suggest that LSD can cause damage to chromosomes although no more significantly than a lot of commonly used substances like aspirin. LSD can also cause 'flashbacks' although there is no evidence to suggest that it causes permanent harm. LSD is a Class A drug. Surveys suggest that as many as ten per cent of those aged fifteen to twenty-four might have tried the drug. It costs £3 to £5 for a tab.

Magic mushrooms
(shrooms, mushies)

These are small, wild mushrooms, the most popular being the Liberty Cap (*Psilocybe semilanceata*). It fruits between September and November throughout the UK. Another popular mushroom is the Fly Agaric (*Amanita muscaria*). They can be eaten raw, cooked, or boiled.

The effects are similar to a mild LSD experience. The variability of the experience and its susceptibility to the user's mood, environment and intentions all apply. While twenty to thirty Liberty Caps are generally required for a full hallucinogenic experience, much fewer may be taken for a milder high and in some cases a few produce the stronger effects. Effects also include euphoria and hilarity. Mushrooms appear not to have any dangerous side-effects. However, distinguishing magic mushrooms from poisonous ones takes some skill.

The mushrooms are not illegal. But their active ingredients psilocin and psilocybin are controlled Class A drugs. It is illegal to boil, crush or make what is known as a 'preparation or other product' containing psilocin or psilocybin. Such a preparation is a controlled substance, subject to the same restrictions and penalties as the drug it contains.

There is evidence of increasing popularity to the point where now perhaps one in ten young people have tried these naturally-occurring hallucinogens.

MDMA
(ecstasy)

MDMA is more commonly known as ecstasy. MDMA is the shortened form of the long chemical name for the drug: 3,4, methylenedioxymethamphetamine. It is one of the 179 drugs that come under the main heading of MDA, phenethylamine. MDA, known as 'snowball', is more hallucinogenic and intense than MDMA. Ecstasy, also known as E, burgers, love doves, disco biscuits and other names, is defined as a hallucinogenic amphetamine because its effects combine those of amphetamine and LSD.

A lot of the ecstasy bought by users has little or no MDMA in it. Over half of the tablets seized by the police contain no MDMA. Some contain LSD, some amphetamine, some ketamine. Others have no drug content whatsoever. It is almost always taken as a tablet or capsule. The look of the tablets changes from week to week and counterfeit tablets are sold widely. Often they have insignia imprinted on them, e.g. a dove, a smiley face, or an E.

The type of experience, good or bad, often depends on the mood of the user. In moderate doses, it evokes strong feelings of empathy and a heightened perception of surroundings without the visual distortions and illusions associated with LSD. It is popular with all-night dancers because it increases heart rate and keeps people awake for long periods, elements that go with the kind of music played in clubs where ecstasy takers go. (The music often has a repetitive beat, not unlike a heart rate beat.) It can cause sweating, dry mouth and throat, and raised blood pressure. Because of the amphetamine-like effects of ecstasy, once the drug has worn off, the user may feel fatigue and depression, but these are temporary. It is not a drug that causes physical dependence.

The ecstasy deaths that are known about, are mostly caused by hyperthermia – heatstroke. A few people have died as a result of the stimulant effect of the drug which can cause high blood pressure and heart attacks or brain haemorrhages. Another cause of death is the result of drinking too much water, causing the brain to swell. It's safer to drink small quantities regularly than a large amount at once. Anybody with the following conditions is advised not to take ecstasy: hypertension, heart disease, diabetes, diminished liver function.

Ecstasy is a Class A drug. The drug has only been seized in quantity since 1988. In 1995, it was the most seized Class A drug in two-thirds of police forces. The price of a tablet is £10 to £25 depending on the locality. Given the numbers of those involved in the new dance culture, the figure for those who have tried the drug at least once must run into hundreds of thousands, if not millions.

MMDA, MBDB and MDEA
These three are like ecstasy but are comparatively mild. MDEA is also known as 'Eve'. There are others in this 'family' of drugs that are occasionally heard about: PMA, DMT and DOM. All are reputedly more potent than MDMA. They are all Class A drugs.

Mescaline
Mescaline is derived from the peyote cactus, native to Mexico. It is dried and cut into slices known as 'mescal buttons'. It can be chewed or boiled into a liquid and drunk. Nowadays, it is usually refined into a powder coloured from white to brown. It is taken in doses of up to 500 mg and the effects are similar to LSD. It is a Class A drug. Mescaline is virtually unheard of in the UK.

Methadone
See opiates

Methylamphetamine
See Amphetamine

Opiates and opioids
Opiates are the group of drugs derived from the opium poppy. Opioids include both opiates and their synthetic 'analogues', e.g. methadone, pethidine. They are prescribed as painkillers, cough suppressants and anti-diarrhoea agents. Opioid powders can be swallowed or dissolved in water and injected. Pure opioids in moderate doses produce a range of generally mild physical effects, apart from their powers as painkillers, and a number of

these are used in general medicine. Like sedatives, they depress nervous system activity, including reflex functions such as coughing, respiration and heart rate. They also dilate blood vessels (giving a feeling of warmth) and cause constipation. Opioids rarely cause medical complications during pregnancy. Withdrawal symptoms in the baby are the most likely cause for concern, but these can usually be coped with or treated easily. They vary according to the particular opiate being used. Opioids include dihydrocodeine, morphine, heroin, codeine etc.

Dihydrocodeine
(DF118)

It is an opiate. It is used medically to alleviate less severe pain and as a cough suppressant. It can be smoked, eaten or injected. It is a Class B drug (unless prepared for injection when it becomes Class A) and as such carries all the implications as described in Chapter Seven. Fourteen per cent of Scotland's drugs misuse database clients took opiates other than heroin and methadone (most notably DF118 and buprenorphine). In England, only two per cent took other opiates.

Heroin
(smack, Harry, 'H', horse, junk, brown)

Heroin is an opiate produced from morphine. Traditionally, it comes in the form of a white powder. A brown coloured powder form of heroin is now being seen on the streets and is cheaper (see Chapter Five). The white form is normally between thirty and eighty per cent pure. It is rare for it to be swallowed by a user because of the effects being relatively weak.

For the greatest 'hit', heroin is dissolved in water and citric acid and heated until it is a clear brown solution. Then it is drawn up in a syringe, often using a cigarette filter to remove impurities, and injected into a vein (the effect here is almost instantaneous), muscle or under the skin. Otherwise it can be smoked or snorted. Snorting allows the user to take the whole dose into the body at once, making it easier to overdose. When smoked, heroin powder is heated on tin foil and the fumes inhaled, commonly through a small tube, a practice known as 'chasing the dragon'. Heroin is an analgesic (painkiller). Its effects last for about three to six hours. Users often describe the feeling to be one of warmth, well-being and safety. Any anxiety and desires disappear.

Heroin has the usual effects attributed to opiates. First use is often accompanied by nausea and vomiting. Repeated injection damages veins, sometimes resulting in thrombosis and abscesses. Also, heroin interferes with the female menstrual cycle but doesn't necessarily prevent someone from getting pregnant. Opiate use during pregnancy results, on average, in smaller babies who may suffer severe withdrawal symptoms after birth. These can usually be managed with supportive therapy (which may or may not involve giving the baby drugs), until the withdrawal syndrome has run its course, but can be fatal in the absence of medical care. Opiate withdrawal during pregnancy can also result in fetal death, so the preferred option is usually to maintain the mother (and therefore the fetus) on low doses of opiates until birth. Heroin is a Class A drug and costs around £80 a gram.

Methadone
(juice, linctus)

This is a synthetic opiate used as a heroin substitute. It is usually taken in syrup form but it can also be prescribed as tablets, although doctors are advised not to prescribe them by the Department of Health because they are worth more on the illicit market. It can also come in an injectable form. It has the usual effects attributed to the opiates which last for about twenty-four hours. Methadone is less intense but has a longer-lasting effect than heroin. There is no evidence to show that there is any additional risk in having a baby while on a stable dose of methadone. It is a Class A drug and costs around £10 for 50 ml.

Morphine
This is an effective painkiller, from which it is not difficult to produce heroin, and is derived from opium. It is a Class A drug and may be found in powder, tablet, liquid or ampoule form. Illicit users take the drug by swallowing tablets, drinking a liquid form, injecting it, heating and inhaling the vapour, or even by using a suppository.

PCP
(angel dust, peace pill)

PCP's full chemical name is phencyclidine. It is manufactured as a veterinary anaesthetic. It is either eaten in powder form or injected. The user experiences a trance-like state, with sensations of weightlessness, detachment, diminished body size and an overall distortion of perception. There may also be feelings of overwhelming excitement and strength. Overdosing can cause vomiting, agitation, disorientation, respiratory depression and convulsions. PCP is very rare in the UK. It is a Class A drug.

Solvents and volatile substances

Solvents are chemicals which give off vapour or gas at room temperature, and can be inhaled through the mouth or nose. Volatile substance abuse is where such a substance is used to achieve intoxication.

They can be anything from fast drying glues, correcting fluid and thinner, lighter fuel, shoe and metal cleaners and polish, to propellant gases found in aerosol sprays. The solvents are sniffed. The effects can be heightened by increasing the concentration of vapour and/or excluding air by sniffing from a plastic bag held at the mouth or nose and in some instances placed over the head, an extremely dangerous method of transmission. Equally dangerous is spraying the chemicals straight into the mouth. They produce feelings of intoxication not unlike drunkenness, a sense of being high, occasionally hallucinatory experiences, and euphoria. They also make people sick, dizzy and drowsy.

They are not illegal, although it is against the law to sell to known or suspected young solvent misusers. Several recent British studies have found that between five and ten per cent of secondary school pupils have tried solvents. Solvents cause more deaths than any other recreational drugs apart from alcohol and tobacco.

Tobacco

Tobacco is made of the dried leaves of the nicotiana plant. It is most often smoked, but can be chewed or in the case of snuff (powdered tobacco), sniffed. The drug effect of tobacco is caused by nicotine, but cigarette smoke also consists of droplets of tar, carbon monoxide and other gases. Nicotine and other substances are absorbed by the lungs, so how much smoke is absorbed depends on how much smoke is actually inhaled rather than 'puffed'.

Nicotine is a drug with complex effects on brain activity. It is absorbed from the lungs rapidly enough for each inhalation to have an almost instantaneous and separate effect. One or two cigarettes increase pulse rate and blood pressure, reduce appetite, lower skin temperature and produce symptoms of stimulation and arousal. Tolerance rapidly develops and the more one smokes, the more likely one is to suffer from heart disease, blood clots, heart attacks, lung infections, strokes, bronchitis, bad circulation, lung cancer, cancer of the mouth and throat and ulcers.

Tobacco contributes to at least 100,000 premature deaths in the UK every year: a quarter of all young male cigarette smokers die 'before their time' due to tobacco. Women who smoke beyond the first months of pregnancy tend to give birth to smaller and less mature babies which may give rise to difficulties after the birth. It is now well established that the population is at risk from the effects of passive smoking ranging from respiratory irritations, infections and asthma (especially in children) through to cancer.

Selling any tobacco products to children under sixteen is prohibited. However, even children who cannot legally be sold tobacco can legally buy, possess and smoke it. About thirty per cent of people aged sixteen or over are smokers. Nearly one in five men and one in ten women smoke sufficiently (more than twenty cigarettes a day) to be classed as heavy smokers. In 1994 twenty-six per cent of fifteen year-old boys and thirty per cent of fifteen year-old girls were found to be regular smokers. Of the younger children, aged between eleven and fifteen, the figure is twelve per cent, a slight rise in the 1990s.

Special thanks must go to the ISDD for their help in compiling this glossary.

Where to go for help

For free confidential advice or help and details of your local drug services, call the National Drugs Helpline 0800 776600. They keep a database covering the whole of the British Isles.

National organisations

Institute for the Study of Drug Dependence (ISDD)
32-36 Loman Street
London SE1 0EE
Tel: 0171 928 1211
The ISDD has a library service and publishes material on most aspects of drugs. It also sells publications on behalf of other organisations. Call the above number for a catalogue of publications.

Standing Conference on Drug Abuse
(SCODA)
32-36 Loman Street
London SE1 0EE
Tel: 0171 928 9500
SCODA provides specialist advice on local drug services and information on drug treatment and care, prevention and education.

Alcoholics Anonymous
(for England and Wales)
General Service Office of AA
PO Box 1
Stonebow House
York YO1 2NJ
Tel: 01904 644026

Scottish Service Office of AA
Baltic Chambers
50 Wellington Street
Glasgow G2 6HJ
Tel: 0141 2219027

AA Central Office
(for Northern Ireland)
152 Lisburn Road
Belfast BT9 6AJ
Tel: 01232 681084

ADFAM National
32-36 Loman Street
London SE1 0EE
Tel:0171 928 8900
ADFAM is a charity for families and friends of drug users. It provides confidential support and information about drugs and local services nationwide. A helpline is provided on the above number on weekdays from 10 am to 5 pm.

Families Anonymous
Unit 37
Doddington and Rollo
Community Association
Charlotte Despard Avenue
Battersea
London SW11 5JE
Tel: 0171 498 4680
Advice and self-help groups for friends and families of drug users. The office is staffed Monday to Friday from one to six in the afternoon. There is an answer phone for contact outside office hours.

British Association for Counselling (BAC)
1 Regent Place
Rugby
CV21 2PJ

BAC holds a directory of counselling resources. Enquiry by letter only. For a list of counsellors in your area, write in enclosing an SAE.

Narcotics Anonymous
UK Service Office
PO Box 198J
London N19 3LS
Tel: 0171 498 9005
This is a network of self-help groups for drug users based on the AA model.

Release
388 Old Street
London EC1V 9LT
Tel: 0171 729 9904
24 hr service 0171 603 8654
A national 24-hour telephone helpline for advice and information on drug-related problems, especially legal ones. They also produce a series of publications, a catalogue of which can be obtained from them. Publications include *Drugs and the Law*, *At the Police Station* and fact sheets about specific drugs.

Re-Solv
30A High Street
Stone
Staffordshire ST15 8AW
Tel: 01785 817885
Provides general information and educational material on solvent and volatile substance misuse.

TACADE (The Advisory Council on Alcohol and Drug Education)
1 Hulme Place
The Crescent
Salford
Manchester M5 4QA
Tel: 0161 745 8925

TACADE works in the field of personal, social and health education, particularly alcohol and drug education.

Youth Access
1A Taylors Yard
67 Alderbrook Road
London SW12 8AD
Tel: 0181 772 9900
This organisation is able to refer young people to their local counselling service. They hold a list of approximately 350 services throughout the country.

Scotland

Scottish Drugs Forum
5 Waterloo Street
Glasgow G2 6AY
Tel: 0141 221 1175
Provides details of drugs services in Scotland.

Wales

Welsh Drug and Alcohol Unit
4th Floor
St Davids House
Wood Street
Cardiff CF1 1EY
Tel: 01222 667766
Provides details of drugs services in Wales.

Northern Ireland

Research Group on Chemical Dependency
Graham House
1-5 Albert Square
Belfast BT1 3EQ
Tel: 01232 240900
Provides details of drugs services in Northern Ireland.

The Republic of Ireland

A full and detailed list of drug services in the Republic of Ireland is available in the form of a *Directory of Alcohol, Drug and Related Services in the Republic of Ireland*, free of charge from the Health Promotion Unit, Department of Health, Hawkins House, Dublin 2   Tel: 01 671 4711

AA Dublin Service Office
109 South Circular Road
Leonards Corner
Dublin 8
Tel: 01 453 8998

Addresses and telephone numbers of agencies mentioned in this book

Bristol Drugs Project
11 Brunswick Square
Bristol BS2 8PE
Tel: 0117 987 1500

Edinburgh Harm Reduction Team
22-24 Spittal Street
Edinburgh EH3 9DU
Tel: 0131 537 8326

Enhance RDP
(Recreational Drugs Programme)
123 West Street
Glasgow G5 8BA
Tel: 0141 429 8321

Kaleidoscope Youth and Community Project
40-46 Cromwell Road
Kingston-upon-Thames
Surrey KT2 6RE
Tel: 0181 549 2681/7488

Lifeline Manchester
101-103 Oldham Street
Manchester M4 1LW
Tel: 0161 839 2054

Network Drugs Advice Project
Abbey House
361 Barking Road
Plaistow E13 8LE
Tel: 0171 474 2222

Swindon Parents Against Drugs
Tel: 01793 536090

Trafford Piper Project
25 Edge Lane
Stretford M32 8HN
Tel: 0161 865 3322

Unit 51
36 Portland Street
Huddersfield HD1 5PL
Tel: 01484 510826

Picture Acknowledgements

Corbis-Bettmann: **57**
Corbis-Bettmann/UPI: **15**
Corbis: **W. Conway, 28; Dan Lamont, 156**

Camera Press: **13, 20, 49, 53, 93, 104, 107, 110, 114, 129, 132, 136, 144**

Format: **Frances Lang, 38; Sacha Lehrfreund, 48; Maggie Murray, 42; Joanne O'Brien, 37; Miriam Reik, 54; Lisa Woollett, 29, 64, 147**

John Frost Newspapers: **25, 59, 66, 134**

HIT: **16, 60, 89, 94, 98, 99, 123**

Magnum Photos: **Stuart Franklyn, 55, 56; Leonard Freed, 32; Peter Marlow, 105, 109; Eugene Richards, 135**

Network: **Mike Goldwater, 138**

Rex Features: **9, 62, 69, 71, 73**